American Writers Review 2020

March 2021

American Writers Review 2020

D Ferrara, Editor
Patricia Florio, Founder

Patricia Florio (signature)

To Grace, who lived her name,

and

all the others taken too soon

Grace by D Ferrara

Contents

iv

v

Special Thanks to the Judges of Our 2020 Writing Contest:

Gregory Fletcher

Lenore Hart

Carol MacAllister

Scott Roskos

A Word from the Team

A year ago, when we joyfully introduced our 2019 issue, no one could have guessed how the world would turn upside down. Had we known the tragedies of the past year, we might not have embarked on the journey that led here. We are glad that we did.

Just a year after losing her father, D lost her mother, possibly to Covid-19. We will never know for sure. Grace was a woman worthy of her name, reserved, yet warm, always welcoming. That loss pales when compared to the death and illness of the world, of course, but the isolation rubs grit on the wound. Patricia's life got upended by difficulties and change, adding chaos as well as lack of most human contacts.

But we survive. Thanks to those who have submitted to this journal, we have even thrived. Our family adjusts, grows, learns to accept. We find new friends, rediscover others, and carry on.

American Writers Review 2020 looks good. Our e-book, *Art In the Time of Covid-19* has helped us endure. We hope you find them as special as we do.

D Ferrara
Patricia Florio

Immense Gratitude to Our Staff:
Kristin Florio
Dale Louise
Brigitte Carroll

.

Alan Sincic
Bob Sanders
Winner, 2020 American Writers Review Contest
Fiction

The lightning struck. The rain
The purpose of this story is to make you want to be friends with the author. Is it good enough yet? Has he succeeded? His name is Bob Sanders and he lives at 2624 Wicker Lane, New Haven, CT 04720 and he would love it if you would come by afterwards for a drink or, if you are not the drinking kind, a cup of hot tea or some cocoa.

The rain fell to the ground. "Heavens to Betsy," said Betsy
So just kick back and relax. Bob cannot begin to tell you how excited he is that you chose him over all those other great writers like Shakespeare and Hemingway you could be reading right now instead of him. What a classy person you are turning out to be! Bob will do his darndest to live up to your high expectations for him and, in the larger sense, for literature as a whole.

said Betsy with a shake of her blonde head,
It goes without saying that Bob here will be as light or as heavy as you like because by golly you are the customer and the customer is always right.

a shake of her head that was blonde,

So if you would like a different noun or verb or whatever then just ask. Bob's been slaving all day over these nouns and verbs his aim being to please but hey–plenty more where that came from! No problem. If there's a word that has been misspelled, then let's work together to catch it now, early on, before things get even more out of control. Is there an indentation where there should not be an indentation? Then Bob will have that indentation removed, by force if necessary, and at whatever cost to his own personal vision.

> Betsy with her blonde hair shaking on her head that was a
> normal color

And at no extra cost to yourself. Wow. And without having to rustle up a single word on your own. Lucky for you! But you deserve it! Bob is more than happy to give you a well-earned rest while he struggles to provide you with the snappy details and the gruff-but-lovable characters that you have come to expect of him, the quirky down-home imagery that is beaten out of him for the sole delight and amusement of...oops. Bob seems to have more nouns and verbs than he realized. Gracious. Bob has been very tired lately. But Bob is not a complainer.

> said bald Betsy

Because nobody wants to be friends with a complainer. Friendship is built on trust. And you can trust Bob when he tells you it's not as glamorous as you think, this life of the raconteur. Henry James suffered from bad digestion. Ernest Hemingway broke three ribs in a plane crash on the African veldt. Bob Sanders can no longer recite his poetry within a hundred feet of the lobby of the Bedford Cineplex or affiliated entities in the State of Connecticut but is Bob Sanders going to let that throw a monkey wrench into the burning fire of his (Bob Sanders') heart? In your dreams!

> Betsy as she ran through the rain. "Wait up, you handsome-
> looking Detective Sands who only recently became my
> boyfriend," she said. Suddenly

So fasten your seatbelts because here we go.

> "Bang –

If you are a pregnant woman, a person with a heart condition, or a child under 42", you just might want to step out of line right now before we kick this baby up into overdrive

"Bang-Bang!" Betsy screamed. Detective Sands went crashing through a window

If you are reading this and happen to be a movie producer that thing about the window breaking don't be worried. You could get a stunt window and a stunt person so that nobody would get hurt. And an action star like Burt Reynolds would be good in the part of the detective because he does all his own stunts. That way you save money.

as glass went flying everywhere. "Ouch," said hard-boiled Detective Sands

Sometimes they fly the writer to Hollywood to be there on the set while they make the movie. A good idea, since the writer knows how the words go and could even explain to Burt Reynolds what he (the writer) was thinking during the writing of the story.

he said to his humorous sidekick Spongy. "I have just been shot by a bullet and gone crashing through a window."

Some writers, like Shakespeare or like, say, Bob Sanders for example, have done a little acting in their own spare time and in, like, an emergency, if, say, Burt Reynolds broke his leg or something, they could step right in and do the part themselves. Plus they already know what happened in the story. A double savings!

"Goodness gracious," said Spongy humorously,

So you're wondering would Bob object to the using of for instance his likeness on the billboards for the movie the answer would be no if it was done out of friendship and not Hollywood-type friendship either but real friendship. For a friend Bob would be more than happy to visit the TV talk shows and such to share humorous anecdotes about the movie, the book, the writing process, hopes and dreams and wishes and so forth. And as far as a limo for the Oscars and all go, not to worry. Good old Bob Sanders would just as soon drive his own self in his own beat-up old down-home car and if you ask why, because that's the kind of guy he is, is why.

"*Ouch* is right, you hard-boiled, brown-haired, six-foot two-inch detective, you," said Spongy jokingly

Though that's not happening till the movie was done,

to the Cleveland-born Detective Sands,

which depending on the book being done

an '87 graduate of Sandusky Community College

being dependent on the individual sentences

with a degree in Animal Husbandry

like this one

and a minor in

making it to the end without running out of the stuff that goes into them in the first place, meaning

Detectiving.

words. Mercy. Talk about a pressure. But a good pressure in Bob's case, a fun pressure, Bob being a fun-loving, free-wheeling kind of guy. Creativity is Bob's middle name. Carpe Diem! Just think of the words in all the other stories that Bob has already produced, like that one about the man drinking the cup of coffee and trying to get it to just the right amount of cream on the inside. You liked that story, didn't you? Go back and look at that story. Compare the two stories. Do you think that there has been a falling off in Bob's talent? Maybe he was never very good to begin with. Maybe he should go back to the job in the hardware store. Is this what it would take to make you happy?

Bang! The owner of the hardware store clutched his breast and crumpled to the

Oy vey! Sakes alive. Cowabunga. It would be very easy for Bob to say "Go on, charge on, charge on ahead and gallop right over the feelings of Bob Sanders. You are a daring and artistic soul. Please do not bruise the tip of your finger as you reach for another toasted cheese puff." It would be easy to say that but Bob not is going to say that because Bob is a peach of a guy.

ground. Down to the ground he crumpled as Detective Sands

A peach of a guy just warning you not to be fooled by friends who pretend to be friends but bail when you need them the most.

> good old Detective Sands along with Spongy and his (Detective
> Sands', not Spongy's) girlfriend Betsy jumped into their fancy
> racecar to racecar themselves away from the broken glass in the
> other sentence and onto the hardware store, just in time to
> catch the pretty checkout girl

So be careful. You've gotten (those of you who are innocent) a warm feeling these last few paragraphs we've been together. But life is more than a warm feeling. A bunch of words on a page is no substitute for love. And what good is a warm feeling if you've got nobody to get warm and feely about? So snap out of it.

> standing over the body with a smoking gun in her hand. "Come
> with me," commanded Detective Sands

You don't want to grow old and die all alone, now do you? Goodness gracious. There's a great big old world out there just full of people wanting to be your friend. So get cracking!

> "Me. Come with me," commanded Detective Sands
> commandingly. "Like on a date?" said the attractive slim-figured
> hardware checkout girl to

"But I don't know how to make friends," you say. "I am so pathetic." Don't be silly. If you were to start, say, with somebody you already know (like say Bob Sanders), then you could just write them a letter to say how much you are liking whatever it is you happen to be doing this moment an example being, say, reading this story by

> the ruggedly handsome detective

Bob Sanders.

In the letter you could say how anybody who managed to come up with such attractive nouns and verbs and stuff must also probably be an attractive person in the physical sense, direct and in person. In the letter you could say how refreshing it is to come across a writer who is so open and personable. Remember, on the printed page, Bob may not seem to be such a vividly realized character, but in person you would find him much more concrete and specific than anybody could have expected. Even more so.

"Yes, yes–a date," said the ruggedly handsome detective as he swept her up into his rugged arms and gave her a big kiss.

"Wow!" said girlfriend number one to girlfriend number two, "another extra girlfriend for my boyfriend Detective Sands!"

Gosh. And if you were a letter and your car was an envelope, you could just up and mail yourself to 2624 Wicker Lane, exit 27 off I-75 south! Wouldn't that be something?

Up into his other arm she jumped, the one not holding the pretty checkout girl. "You are just too much man for one woman!"

If you get here and Bob doesn't answer, come right on in anyway and make yourself at home. The key is under the garden gnome with the wheelbarrow, over to the left of the mailbox. There's a carafe of pasteurized orange juice in the fridge, cups in the cabinet above the sink. Help yourself to any snacks (the tropical fruit and nut mix is particularly good) and feel free to peruse Bob's collection of 1930s roadside diner placemats.

"Three cheers for Detective Sands," cheers the crowd. The Pope looks down from his balcony and waves. Even though he is wounded, Detective Sands

If you are a publisher (or would like to be one), feel free to check the second drawer from the bottom of Bob's dresser where you can find his unpublished poems, notes, hopes, wishes, and dreams. Help yourself! What a surprise it will be when Bob finds his work suddenly appearing in print! And in your magazine!

still manages, though wounded, seriously wounded, to throw chocolates to the busload of orphans pulling up to the crime scene. "Look at that arm," exclaims Hall of Fame Orioles third baseman

Bob's dog Scooter will be delighted to lick your hand and scamper gaily 'round your pant cuffs because any friend of Bob's is a friend of Scooter's. If you are the appropriate gender (entirely your decision Bob not being one to pressure) feel free to slip into something comfortable,

pour yourself a glass of wine, and drape yourself seductively across the
Barcalounger to wait for Bob to

> ejaculates Hall of Fame Orioles third baseman Cal Ripkin, Jr.
> admiringly: "Hell of an arm!" "Good work, Sandy-man," barks
> gruff Police Commander Sean Connery, co-starring Harrison Ford
> as Spongy. Suddenly

to pop up, for Bob to pop up. Or slip into the kitchen to bake him a hot
apple pie an apron slung over your shoulder to wipe the crumbs from his
cheek when

> the wounded Detective Sands crumples to the ground. How
> brave of him to make it even this far. The girlfriends scoop him
> up into their four breasts and carry him up the steps to

wipe the crumbs, wipe the crumbs from his cheek when he finally
arrives. If you're unpacking your suitcase in the front bedroom you might
want to lay out your socks and underwear on the bed first

> the podium where General Douglas MacArthur presents the
> Congressional Medal of

so that you'll be more comfortable. If you're giving birth don't hesitate to
kick back on the comfy Appalachian quilt because gosh don't you think
you deserve it after all

> Medal of Honor to the brave but just about practically dying
> Detective Sands who refuses saying

after all you've been through. And if the baby just happens to turn out to
be,

> "Aw, shucks, Mother Teresa. Here—you deserve this more than
> me." The orphaned children cheer. The cameras flash. The
> crowd shouts

if it just so happens that it turns out to be Bob Sanders, do not be shy
about introducing yourself

> "Bob Sanders! Bob Sanders! Bob Sanders!"

he is crying pick him up

> shouting "Bobbie-Bob-Bob!"

lift him up

> as they lift him up

carry him off
        on their shoulders
to take him
        raise him
home with you
        up saying
raise him up
        Bobbie oh Bobbie sweet baby a baby
as your
        of my
very
        very
own
        own.

Colin Pink
The View from London
Poetry

I Yowl

That yowling cat at five-fifty AM pulled the stopper
on sleep. Its quavering wails a cross between pain
and desire, the rise and fall of distress and fear or
frustration made it impossible to climb back into
the bottle of oblivion. It unwittingly sang the mood
of the city. Suddenly it stopped. I made a cup of tea.

II Normal

This month I had lots of plans; now they're all dust,
seem dated like a fifties girdle or a mullet haircut.
The phones keep cutting out, the supermarket shelves
are suddenly empty. Something ripped the page off
the calendar and the new picture is unlike any other.
What was normal, taken for granted, recedes from sight
to be replaced by something far less comfortable,
a thing which I fear might become the new normal.

III Revolving

The revolving door of time flips open
the pages of the seasons. One by one,
before our vision, the zoetrope of life
unfolds its flickering images, dancing
in a circle that seems eternal like the
devotion of the waves licking the shore.

*Random Person at Dubai International Airport: Proxy
for All* Drawing by Raul J. Mendez

Molly Fuller
The Darkness of Rivers
Fiction

I'm near the edge of the silt-dark Ohio river, visiting my hometown, standing in line at the neighborhood store and I'm tapping my foot when my body suddenly remembers, and I feel my limbs give over into the slower tick of Appalachian time. I'm admiring the unsmiling humans pasted to the wall near the cash register, stills, apparently, from the security camera dangling above the Exit sign. A card above the photos says, "bad check writers."

Unlike those grimacing people, I have a resting smiling face, which is a problem that constantly attracts strangers. I see a guy I might vaguely know from childhood looking at me. He's wearing a button-down shirt, un-tucked, jeans, a baseball cap, and he looks like every guy who has ever tried the line he uses next.

"You look good enough to eat," he says, walking up a little too close.

I can feel myself making a face. "I'm not sure what you mean."

"You look sweet," he says. "Like dessert."

Usual me would be gone already, but I'm in a kind of mood. I'm in a mood because I'm in this particular town on this particular day to bury my best childhood friend who jumped off a bridge. He wasn't sad when I knew him, but I guess everything got to be too much for him. Maybe the weather for one thing. It's always so grey around here.

Maybe the food for another. The fancy, out-to-eat joint is Applebee's. Maybe it was genetics, or drugs, or a breakup. I don't know and I guess I never will. He didn't call me before he did it. So, when what's-his-name tells me I look like cake or pie or something, I am ready to feel some other way about any other thing.

"Want to get out of here?" I ask. He stares at me. I shake my hair out of my face, say, "What? That shitty line never worked before?" He still has nothing to say. "Do you have a car?" I ask, my hand poised to stash my would-be purchase into the candy display.

Dude comes out of his stupor, says, "Yeah," pulls keys out of his pocket and kind of jingles them in my face, like you might do with a baby.

I swat at them and say, "Let's go." I turn on my heel, heading straight toward the door. I smile up at the camera and don't bother to see if he's following me. I know he is.

We get in a red Mustang of some vintage. "Where are we going?" he asks.

I open my window, lean my elbow on the edge, say, "Just drive east out of town." The night is black outside. No moon. No stars. Dead black.

"Do I know you?" he asks, putting the car in gear.

"No," I say.

"Tell me your name," he says.

I do a hair flip, purse my lips and let out a stream of air. "Call me Sam," I say. "Do you smoke?" I ask.

He shakes his head.

"Stop up here," I say, pointing at a gas station.

He moves to turn on the radio.

"Don't," I say, pushing his hand away.

I like the silence. I'm listening to the sound of the road under the tires, trying to match the sound with what I feel through the frame of the car, the cushions on the seat, all the stuff between me and the hard road.

After he pulls into the gas station parking lot, I step out into a low hum of insects attracted to the ungodly bright fluorescents lighting up the pumps and the dirty, pressed-gum and cigarette-butt-littered cement. I watch as some of the moths throw themselves into the light and fall to the ground. One floats gently in the wind, lands on the ground in front of me, and I swear it is as big as my hand. I stand there staring at it, the black dot surrounded by a larger blue dot on the back of its wing almost like an eye and I think about my friend. I try to remember the color of his eyes but I can't.

I buy a pack of Camels, no girly light ones for me, thanks, I like to know where the end is coming from. My friend and I had that in common. As I tap the pack against the inside of my wrist, I am calmed by this ritual. I get back in the car.

"Where to?" he asks.

I point my arm straight ahead, like someone directing traffic.

We go a few miles; I gesture to the right. He turns the wheel sharply and I feel it in my whole body. I'm wondering why he's putting up with me, with this, what is wrong in his head that this seems alright to him.

"Why are you doing this?" I ask.

"You're sexy," he says, putting his arm around me.

"No," I say, pushing his arm away. "Go left here."

Then I see it. The bridge is up ahead, looming in the darkness as the car lights hit it. "Pull over," I say. I have the door open before the car is fully in park.

He opens his door too.

"Wait here," I say. I get out and walk toward the bridge as long grass scratches at my legs. I look back at him, blow a flirty little movie star kiss and wave. I know he can see me, outlined in shadows, lit up by the headlights.

I stand on the side of the road a second before I step over the guardrail and balance my body on the thin cement edge. I hear the sound of water, the sound of shoes on loose gravel. The guy calls, "Sam." I imagine what it would feel like falling into the darkness below. He calls out twice more, closer now, frantic, "Sam, Sam," and my friend's name, like an incantation, echoes across the dark river.

Photograph by D Ferrara

John Urban
The Play or Splay of Words
Poetry

Out of the Eternal, the e(x)ternal.
*

The elf, the higher aspect of the self.
*

The pumpkin, Jupiter's orange spot.
*

The play of words, the play of light on water.

Photograph by Jeff Talarigo

Don Noel
Work Rules
NonFiction

It was early in the Korean War. Halfway through college, I had come "home" to Ohio, a thousand miles from the town in which I'd grown up and graduated high school; my folks had moved during my sophomore year.

I needed to make money that summer toward the college year ahead. Happily, the economy was robust; my recollection is that I lined up the first factory job of my life without needing the intervention of my father—who was of the managerial persuasion but hadn't been in town long enough to be of much help.

I had been three weeks at that job when I overslept. I woke with a sickening jolt an hour after stifling the windup alarm by my bed—far too late to be at work on time. In a teen-age funk, I assumed all was lost.

I was no stranger to work: I'd help drive cattle to summer pastures near the High Sierra in California; had done a day's work unloading hundred-pound grain sacks from a freight car at a Nebraska rail siding; had covered high school sports for the weekly *West Orange Chronicle* in New Jersey and earned a bit more by phoning highlights to the *Newark Evening News*; and had for several years spent a pre-school hour every day mucking out stalls at a nearby riding academy, acquiring a subtle halo of fragrance that hurried showers never entirely expunged.

But this was different: I was a member of the United Rubber Workers, making automobile radiator hose at a BFGoodrich plant in Akron.

Had I been more experienced, I might have hurried into work late, and asked my shop steward to win me clemency. But I was too much the neophyte even to imagine my labor union going to bat for me.

Besides, I had in my first few weeks given both the union steward and the company's floor foreman reason to think that I deserved no favors.

I worked on the walk-up third floor of an ancient factory building. The work space was illuminated partly by harsh fluorescent tubes in a high ceiling, but mostly by a huge outer wall of windows, a checkerboard of small panes with rusty steel mullions, admitting such daylight as could penetrate glass clouded by decades of industrial exhalations and probably never washed. In addition to admitting some light, they offered us a fuzzy, grimy adumbration of our nearest neighbor, another once-red brick factory building adjoining ours.

The ceilings were high because most of the machines densely packed on the floor—at least several dozen, as I recall—were in part powered by belts of industrial leather that linked heavy drive wheels on each machine to equally heavy wheels whirring on room-length axles overhead. The cavernous space was cacophonously noisy and of course dirty. We splashed solvents and adhesives onto our products; I shudder to wonder what evil dusts and toxicities—by today's standards—filled the air we unsuspectingly and innocently inhaled.

My partner on a two-man machine was nicknamed Cherry. A short, clean-shaven black man with close-cropped hair that showed work experience.

Our task was monotonously straightforward: We spread out long, narrow layers of textured rubber fabric down the length of the table, ready to be coaxed between steel rollers that also ran the length. We applied adhesives and helped the machine roll twenty-foot-long tubes that gradually grew thicker and stronger as we glued on additional layers. We scurried back and forth to tend and adjust as each tube grew in heft.

I soon devised a way—details have long escaped me—that enabled both of us to shorten our peregrinations the length of our machine. Being thus more efficient, we could complete each tube in perhaps a minute's less time. For me, it was an opportunity to apply my mind, enlivening an otherwise deadeningly repetitive series of tasks.

I would like to think that my workmate Cherry also enjoyed a variation on the tedium he had endured far longer than I; at least he did not complain about my innovations.

Others did.

When we took a bathroom break–a prize the union had won years back–the shop steward joined us to brusquely explain the error of our ways. Each machine had a well-established quota, and men were penalized if they failed to maintain that pace. I might suffer no lasting pain by speeding up the process. But in a few weeks, the steward knew, I'd go back to college, leaving poor Cherry to work his ass off or be docked.

Worse, the company might bring in its god-damned efficiency experts to study the shortcuts I'd devised, and might make everyone, on every machine, hustle more–a price I wouldn't be around to pay.

I got the picture; I remember being genuinely chastened and fulsomely apologetic. Cherry and I went back to making tubes the usual way, taking care not to hurry, working by the rules.

So here I was, in early morning a few weeks later, not in the least confident I had won back the union's heart – and imagining that the foreman, having noticed our brief burst of efficiency and subsequent slowdown, would be ill-disposed to tolerate my tardiness.

I was in the kitchen, despondently nursing a glass of milk, remembering the price tags in the college bookstore where I had checked out the texts required for my fall courses, wondering how I would earn enough money to buy those books now that I'd lost my first real job. I was, in short, wallowing in failure when my mother came downstairs.

What was I doing here? she demanded.

I tried to explain; she brushed aside my stammering. Did I know the foreman's name? I did. Did I know the factory's phone number? I didn't. She pushed the phone book at me: Look it up. I did. Now dial that number, she instructed, and tell the operator you want to speak to the foreman—by name.

I did as she said. After a nervous moment, my call was duly transferred upstairs; my foreman answered the phone. He may have guessed, but he couldn't see my shaking hands and may not have known how tremulously inadequate I felt. As Mom had ordered, I apologized, promising it would never happen. Never mind the bus, I said, one of my parents would drive me and I could be there in not much more than fifteen minutes; could I come to work?

Miraculously, he said yes! Get my ass down there right away, and he'd figure out some appropriate punishment for my lateness. Hurry! I did, of course. In a blur of rush-hour traffic and then a frantic dash up those three flights of factory stairs, I was soon reunited with Cherry. The shop steward came by to inquire solicitously about my health and my brief absence—and then to remind me that there was no requirement that we resurrect our shortcuts to make up for lost production. The union, he promised, had my back.

In the years since, as a journalist, I've had occasion to remember that moment when reporting on inner-city kids who lost their jobs for minor sins such as tardiness. An important key to getting kids off the streets and into productive lives, I observed, was to assign them wise counselors who could coax them through occasional lapses.

They were no worse than I; all any of them lacked was a mother who knew how to stiffen their spines, and could teach them how to overcome error by appealing to bosses' better natures.

The rest of that summer in Akron was, with one small exception, uneventful. I was thereafter scrupulously punctual. Cherry and I made radiator hose at the prescribed pace, and I bought him a beer after work now and then. Neither the shop steward nor the foreman had further occasion to be annoyed with the college kid.

The exception to the routine of every day: The union found fault, as the summer progressed, with some work rule that didn't affect me. I cannot at this point even remember what it was. I assured my workmates of my support—even when it appeared the union might call a strike over the dispute, and I might again face the prospect of empty pockets at the college bookstore.

And then strike we did: The Akron plant of the BFGoodrich Company was shut down for exactly two days at the end of the summer. I was assigned a few hours' placard duty on a picket line that was, I thought, remarkably thinly populated.

It was, I am sure, a mere coincidence that the days we were on strike happened to coincide with the opening of the deer hunting season. But when the dispute was mysteriously resolved and we were back at work, many of my workmates, Cherry included, told me they had fresh venison in their freezers.

I spent another few weeks on that factory floor, then bid my machine partner and my other union friends farewell and went back to college.

Nothing in my next semester's academic work matched the education I had that summer.

Photograph by Jeff Talarigo

Matthew Byrne
The Death of the Tie
Poetry

> At its funeral I will bow my head in faux
> melancholy, marching down the row
> of grieving CEO's, politicians, salesmen—
> shaking hands, offering condolences,
> snickering inside at the openly coffined
> tie. Until then, I will observe impatiently
> its fateful unravelling from our necks.
> No longer do we need this ornamental
> phallic symbol pointing to its smallish
> muse. Its slow-but-sure recession won't
> even make the news. Bon voyage I say
> in the mirror as I try for the third time
> to knot the thing correctly, breaking out
> into the pre-meeting sweat of hypocrisy.

Matthew Byrne
Laugh Track
Poetry

I am the sheep dog nudging your return
to the flock. My DNA will not let you stray.
I am the broadcast jab of thunderclap
entreating you back indoors. Without me
you would drift out to sea. Do not think
me dictatorial, but a canal carved for you,
a chime to color in the invisibility of wind.
Knowing what's best for you is how I do.
I am a syringe for the best kind of medicine,
a tourniquet inflating the most viable vein,
the apple a day keeping not laughing away.

Nicolas D. Sampson
Timberwolf
Fiction

Somebody once told me, 'If you're gonna die, die with your boots on.' His name was Eddie, an ex-Marine, and he was a crazy, gruff son of a bitch who practiced what he preached, even if it killed him.

Let me explain. A few months ago I got a call from a man named Jim—'Yeah, just Jim,' he said, and I said, 'You got it!'—informing me that Eddie had died in a shooting incident in Phoenix, Arizona, the day before. Just Jim asked me if I was interested in attending the funeral. I said, 'Yes.' He gave me the details and added I should wear shoes with laces, and that I should tie them. My next words should have been, 'How did you get my number and who's your dealer?' but all I could think about was Eddie—gone!

It was a shock but hardly a surprise. Eddie was the kind of guy who put himself in volatile situations and pissed on the odds. True to form, as I later found out, he'd been walking somewhere in south Tempe, on his way to the grocery store, when he spotted a gang of punks outside a tattoo parlor in the plaza terrorizing the passers-by. He walked over and told them to pack up and leave. They told him to fuck off. He told them to drop dead and they attacked him, all five of them at once. He knocked two of them to the ground before the other three got their guns out and shot him seventeen times.

Was it worth it? Getting gunned down like a dog by some crank-wired kids over what–nothing! Principle, street rep, and nine square feet of sidewalk.

A life has got to be worth more than that.

The funeral was in Eddie's hometown, Lincoln, Illinois.

I told my wife I had to do this. 'We go way back,' I said, not wanting to get into the details. She wasn't happy. It was our daughter's premiere in the school play where she played Ariel, and it killed me not to be there, but I couldn't pit death against a school play. I needed to pay my respects to an old friend no matter how inconvenient. It was the right thing to do.

It was a fine summer day, all sun and fresh prairie air. Eddie would have enjoyed himself. He loved sunny weather, ergo Phoenix, far away from where he was born, and where he would now be laid to rest.

I arrived late and hung over. People were lining up to pay their respects to the deceased. The parlor was jam-packed with folks from all over the country. I met some of them in the line to the casket. Coast-to-coast people. A middle-aged Kentucky State Trooper in his gray uniform and hat. A young woman from Washington in a charcoal-gray cotton dress. A vigorous grandpa from Arizona, wrapped tight in his pressed blue jeans and starched black shirt, and a married couple from Florida who held hands and wore matching print designs. People from all walks of life. They were reserved and polite, conveying grief, a kind of intimacy with each other, most of all with the deceased. Eddie had made a good name for himself. These people were his friends, not mere acquaintances, paying their final respects with solemn faces and an air of privacy that brought everyone together in hushed consternation.

None of his blood relations had showed up. Only friends–his only family.

People asked me how I knew Eddie. I explained how I'd met him at Arizona State University in a psychology class. We were part of the same study group, and his vibrancy and organizational skills were key in acing our field assignments. When I broke up with my girlfriend he gave me perspective and the tools to pick myself up and get back in the game.

The line in the church moved slowly. The room smelled of cologne, perfume and wax, scented oil, and a ton of bad breath. Drafts of halitosis with a splash of mouthwash and digested breakfast. The chalk-white walls swayed in the candlelight, and I felt dizzy. I inched my way ahead, hands clasped forward. A breeze of roses lifted my spirits. A whiff of orange blossoms and mint. Bundles of blood-red roses and white roses and tiny creamy blossoms in tiny wicker baskets. The smell of summer and anniversaries mixed with mourning. The fragrance intensified as we inched our way to the jet-black casket.

People were taking their time saying goodbye, holding brief conversations with the deceased. The Kentucky State Trooper approached the casket with a solemn expression. 'Nice boots!' he drawled, stood solid for half a minute, nodded at the casket and marched away.

It was my turn. I stepped forward and tripped, almost knocking over the casket. I realized that my laces were undone and the grandpa from Arizona had been standing on them. He apologized, I apologized, we smiled at each other. I approached the casket, peeking inside.

Sure enough my old friend's body lay lifeless inside, donned in a navy blue suit, white shirt, a black tie lining his chest, a red handkerchief exploding on the side, face calm, shaved, his jaw set firm and authoritative, crowned with a thin smile. His hair was black and short, with salt streaks. His hands were clasped on his chest. On his middle finger sat his corps ring, dense as a kettle bell. It had served him loyally as a stun gun in close combat and as a chick magnet in the aftermath of victory. His pants, pressed flat and crisp, were like expensive wrapping paper, and underneath them shone his magnificent boots, a casket all boot, just like he'd promised. Clean and shiny, ceremonial, unmistakably seasoned and full of trench life force.

I stared at those boots for a long time. Underneath the gloss I could see the wear and tear and tenacity, the stubbornness of gritted teeth that absorbed the pain with feet planted firm in the ground, not giving in to anything, no matter what.

Yes indeed, Eddie the warrior had fought his way through life, living by his words, practicing what he preached all the way to the grave.

It was small consolation, but crucial, something that gave meaning to his untimely death.

It struck me that he wasn't wearing his uniform. His attire was a simulacrum, but it felt intentional, as if he'd picked the garments himself. I wondered what had driven his choice. Maybe Just Jim knew, but I hadn't met the guy in person, and didn't know what he looked like, and wasn't in a rush to find out.

I leaned in to pay my final respects when—there's no easy way to put it—Eddie opened his eyes and looked at me with a puzzled grin and said, 'Why the long face? Someone die?'

I froze. My limbs went numb and my mind blank, words stuck in my throat. Eddie smiled, grabbed me by the arm, pulled me in close and said, 'Remember to tie your laces tight, son. It's more important than painting your boots slick or wearing the right color shoes. There'll be plenty of time for that later.' He winked, let go of my arm, closed his eyes and froze stiff.

I remember it like it was yesterday.

My outlook changed after that vision. Life took on new meaning, starting with Eddie's. I realized he hadn't died for pride and a piece of sidewalk. He'd lived by a code and done himself proud. A stroke of bad luck had taken him out too soon, but then again who knows when's too soon or too late? We go when we go. The rest is hogwash and conjecture, wishful thinking that betrays hubris. If we're going to be arrogant, let it be through standing up for something good, like having safe streets to walk through without getting harassed, or respecting people to the point where they think about us after we're gone, touched by our presence. I want to stand up for something, like Eddie. I've been traipsing through life without knowing why, basking in reflected glory, taking what is given to me, my friends and family for granted, everything as a kind of joke. I feel isolated, cut off from other people. I speak the words and hit the cues but there's nothing underneath, no connection. Eddie wasn't like that. He lived alone and had no family, and yet the world came to his funeral.

How many people will come to mine, I wonder.

I don't want my children to grow up thinking about their father and coming up with a shadow. Eddie's death and his words from the grave have taught me the value in getting things done and making things matter. Do, and the sparkle will follow. If it doesn't, the grit's good, too, sometimes better, if you know how to wear it.

'It's all about embracing death, Victor,' he told me over a glass of bourbon many years ago. We were in Timberwolf, next to Arizona State University, having a beer. We'd just finished an assignment and were enjoying the fruits of our labor. 'The secret is to enjoy what you do, whatever it is. To make a difference you've got to be present, and to be present you've got to embrace the void. Death. It's beautiful! Don't be afraid to check out, man. Live every day like you're going to die tomorrow. It makes life sparkle. And when you kick the bucket, you're as present as ever.' He paused and downed his drink, ordered another round. 'Some of the most influential people are dead, son! Remember that.'

His words went over my head that day. They were the ramblings of a drunk guy selling two-bit wisdom.

Now I understand.

My approach is different now. I tie my shoelaces with care every morning. Boots, sneakers, hiking shoes, dress shoes, loafers (no laces), I make sure they fit, and that they can do the job. I wear a belt and carry a wallet, charge my phone and laptop before I go to bed, check the map before heading out, make sure I'm early, drink only enough to take the edge off, keep up with the traffic and weather reports, avoid making fun of people, never skip a meal. I kiss my children every day and tell them I love them. One day I won't be around and I want them to have good memories of me, to pass on the golden feeling to their children when they grow up. They shouldn't have to wait for me to rise up from the casket to give them advice. Here I am, no time to waste. I tell them to check their laces every day. My advice may go over their heads now, but it'll kick in down the line. I tell them sarcasm is good when underused and that the powerful reserve their power for when it's necessary. I make coffee for my wife every morning and make sure to leave a note for her to check her gas tank before setting out for work because she forgets things like that, and my job is to make her life easier, not hound her for forgetting.

I do all these things because life is short and you never know what's ahead, waiting to trip you up.

Sarah Key
Bahia Bustamante Haibun
Poetry

Birth and death were all about us. In that unpeopled place,
without our city sirens or honking traffic, there we were, mother
and daughter, in a Patagonian vastness, acres and acres of new
litters: fox, hare, rhea, penguin, choique, guanaco, sea lion. The
fuzziness surprised us, in the bushes, hidden penguin chicks. We
came within inches of their awkward softness, peeling our
windswept hair away to see. Muting all sound but its own, the
wind whirled us through wonders, from chocolate-grey sea lion
pups squashed between roaring bulls and their harems to bright
white whale bones assembled like puzzles on the beach.

It was our first encounter with a carpet of salicornia, the salty
crunch of the kelly-green seagrass we paused to taste, like hiking
a placenta. Time, rolling like the hills around us, slid me back to
that spring, hot as summer you came, changing my landscape
every hour since. At Bahia Bustamante, we galloped up the
beach on Paloma and Plumita, you, always my little feather,
floating next to me.
Once upon a time "quick" meant "alive," and then it was easier

to see what a "quickening" would mean. You were once a wing-flutter in my gut, now and then, a protest of foot. Now there is that quickening inside you. I feel it everywhere I look.

Your baby's heart chugs
locomotive-fast, running
ahead of our past.

Serenity Photograph by Wendy Carrus

Sarah Key
Mamie's Dill Bread
Poetry

When will she let me knead, press the palm of dough?
Mamie's freckled fingers begin the proofing:

> the yeast freckles in foamy bubbles. I finger-
> pop my pink Bazooka, sweeten the grated

onion's bite. I sprinkle sweetly, however great
my tears, she chops. How she dills its essence:

> dill weed, to be wild and green
> dill seed, to be rooted and round.

I root my face around her waist, my wild
she presses into dough, to be divided between

> my parents. Nothing will divide me from her,
> rising, not once, not twice, three times

we keep rising from the kitchen, await the hollow thump.
All the risen loaves resonate the press of her.

Marina Del Ray Photograph by Brigitte Carroll

Kirby Olson
A Martyr for the Liberal Arts
Fiction

When I arrived at work that Monday, I noticed a pair of soft gray sneakers in the dumpster. They stood up from the rest of the refuse by several inches. Upon closer inspection, there was a body attached to them. It was the body of my dean.

It looked as if he had been thrown off the seventh floor.

I dialed 911. A few seconds later a squad car pulled up and Bernie, the chief of police, asked me what the problem was.

I gestured.

I am only a philosophy professor at a small state college. I had no idea that one day I would be confronted with this. I had known our dean was not popular, but I had loved his dog. I liked his wife. His children seemed to be well-raised. He knew Ezra Pound's work and had been raised as a Lutheran. He had given me raises, and said hello in the morning, and in the afternoon, and we wished each other a good weekend for four years. Then, one day, this.

In the investigation that followed, it appeared that there were several disgruntled specimens in the science department. The technical divisions at the college were also suspect. Some had wanted welding to count as a fine art. Our liberal arts dean had postponed a decision

47

indefinitely. Business wanted memos to count as a communications class. Our liberal arts dean had delayed. We in the liberal arts had regarded the dean as our goalie, and had defended him, as he had defended our métier.

Students would report to him, and argue that they needed an A to transfer to a bigger school. He would never change our grades. This one had not appeared in my class during the semester although he was a fixture at fraternity parties and had generally drunk at least a case of beer on any given evening. That one had appeared only in the gym to play basketball, although he was not on the first-rate team, as he couldn't take direction from the region's leading coach. A pagan in the Bible class refused to read the book. The dean had had a spine. A spine that was now severely crumpled.

Bernie asked me, "When did you first see the sneakers?" They were 812 Walking Shoes, from New Balance,, a Boston company that was the last American shoe factory. The dean was proud to have them, and to support American businesses.

"Bernie, I just saw them first five minutes ago."

I was too shocked to cry.

Ambulance men pulled the small gentleman from the rubble and laid him on a gurney. He was a slight figure, with a goatee. He was a martyr for the liberal arts.

Kirby Olson
After the Divorce
Fiction

A heavy hissing filled the silken room. The two children weren't allowed to see their mother very often, so they were overjoyed at this rare visit. Yet what lay behind the lavender bed curtain, heavy with its forced breath?

"Mother?" Tommy asked.

"Yes?" His mother rose in the bed, like an unformed shadow. She separated the curtains slightly, and peered out. Her face was young, her cheekbones high, looking like Cleopatra to James, who had read Shakespeare at seven.

"Will you come and eat grapes with us on the porch?" James asked.

"No, your mother must stay in the house." She patted James' blond hair and smiled. "You two are getting older than I thought. How old are you?"

"Fourteen," said Tommy.

James added, "Twelve."

Their mother smiled at them as she would at a pair of gingerbread cookies. There was a peculiar scent in the room. It smelled like burning rubber to James, who ran his hand over the lavender lace that enshrouded his mother in her beautiful tomb.

"Is your father coming?" She asked.

James and Tommy looked at each other, not knowing what to say. Their father had let them off at what he had called the empress's palace and had gone down to the corner bar to shoot pool with the unemployed and drink Black Cat Vodka.

"No," James said. "He went to the barber. He had to get his hair cut for the concert tonight with his new wife."

"Is something burning?" asked Tommy.

Their mother rose out of bed, a young woman looking as if she was fresh off the cover of a fashion magazine. She lit a Turkish cigarette and turned to her two boys.

"Your father thinks I'm a witch." She grinned. The two boys chuckled, one slapping the other on the back of the tuxedo.

"This way children, it is time…" She led them through a thickly carpeted hallway, into a large blank room. She stepped out of the room, closed the heavy oaken door between them, and fastened the bolt securely. The lights went out.

Soon the flames began to rise. She was cooking James and Tommy in her oven of love.

Brahna Yassky
How Swimming Saved My Life
NonFiction

I was born again in water; not anointed in a religious ceremony, but essentially slapped by a wave and started a new life.

The first time I really swam, when I learned what it meant to move through the water for an extended period without stopping, was in the summer of 1983. Swimming began as a ritual then, as an antidote to being on fire.

A year and a half before, while boiling water, a flame attached itself to my sleeve. Suddenly my arm felt warm, then hot. I smelled something burning; a mixture of barbeque and melting plastic. The pungent smell was close. Very close. I looked for the source. It was me! For a moment, I stared at the orange flames dangling from the wide sleeve of my pink chenille sweater in disbelief as if it were a separate entity. Yet, I felt the extreme heat. I was on fire! *I AM ON FIRE. I AM ON FIRE,* my mind shouted and I wondered, *should I roll on the floor*? Then, *what if the wood floor catches on fire? I'm here alone*. I quickly gasped for air through my mouth, hyperventilating.

Then I couldn't breathe. So scared, I couldn't move. My brain froze. Hot ice. Time stopped. A spark bounced through the air and landed on the cuff of my pants. My arm stung as if attacked by thousands of bees. The piercing pain spread, every nerve buzzed, my brain reconnected. Trembling, I dashed to the door and ran through the hallway screaming for help. In motion, I heard the sizzle of my flesh and clothes. I smelled my singed hair and smoked skin. The flames spread. Their glow lit the dark landing.

My neighbor Tony rushed down the stairs. He rapidly ripped off my clothes and swatted me with a rough blanket whose large pieces of cloth glued themselves to my body as if holding me together. I vibrated with my own shrill cries. The whirling of sirens combined with my screams. It was a flash in time. It was forever. Fast thumping footsteps, voices, equipment hit the stairs and walls. Men carried me suspended and bumping down the stairs. I felt the cold air blow across my face and out of the edge of an eye saw the red of fire engines and a small crowd of people around me on the street. The EMS lifted me onto a stretcher and loaded me into the darkness of an ambulance that careened to St. Vincent's Hospital, in Greenwich Village.

My thirty-three-year-old body was the detritus of the damage. At the hospital, a priest gave me last rites. This can't be, I thought, I'm Jewish. I felt myself pulled towards a white light and fiercely resisted. I was an artist beginning my career and already supporting myself with my paintings. I needed to make more, do more in my life. In the burn unit for three months, the nurse cut the charred skin off 55% of my burned body daily, with tiny scissors and tweezers like a bird's beak picking, pricking, debriding in preparation for grafting new skin onto my raw flesh.

When released from the hospital as an outpatient, I moved back in with my parents after seventeen years of living on my own, because I could not tend to my wounds, dress myself, or prepare food. I became their dependent child again. Physical and occupational therapy six hours a day, five days a week, for ten months was my outpatient routine. The goal was to prevent scar contraction and gain use of my painting arm, which Dr. Haher had sewn back on when others suggested amputation.

When I went to Dr. Haher's office, a year later, I was still wrapped in Jobst scar compression garments, a four-part, tighter-than-skin ensemble.

I listened as Dr. Haher told me to go to the beach for the summer and let it heal me, to swim every day in the late afternoon. Start living in the world again, she said.

In some ways, I had become comfortable in my isolation, far from my pre-fire life: painting every day, partying every night, exhibiting and selling my work, attending art openings. After the fire, I just wanted to be invisible. My scar compression encasement became my safe house. I felt trepidation about leaving my isolation and the support system of my family. I didn't believe Dr. Haher at first. How could I start living in the world if I never wanted to leave my house? However, she had been right about so many things. I sublet my loft in Tribeca. At thirty- four, I started my life again in a low-key but glamorous beach community in Long Island for the summer.

In the morning, after the initial shock of waking to find myself alone in a little rented cottage, in a town where I didn't know anyone and too self-conscious of my red scars to make friends, I slinked down the block to the roaring ocean. Without my Jobst leggings under my clothes, I rolled up my pants mid-thigh and entered the sea. The clean salty air, clear cold water, the rhythmic low thundering of the waves took over my sensate body. I felt a prickly pleasure just standing there, curling my toes in the wet sand. This was a teaser for the afternoon swim beginning at 4 p.m., when the sun's strength diminished.

In the late afternoon, I pedaled my collapsible bike to Devon Beach. Dismounting, the sweat sticking to my skin, I took my folded bamboo mat, towel and book, and claimed a deserted area on the sand. At 4:30 the sun was still high but more muted, not the blinding light of midday; a winding down light, mellow, mature—not blasting its presence; an embracing light casting a glow on everything, including me. I wore a pink-and-green-striped long-sleeve cotton leotard, instead of a bathing suit, to protect my raw skin from the sun. My new grafted skin sat odd on me.

I submerged myself in the water licking the salt off my upper lip. The temperature of the world changed. Every body of water has its own motion and distinctive characteristics. The initial encounter of those is like finding a new friend and silently acknowledging the mechanics of the relationship. I swam parallel to the shore. From the sand, the current was barely visible but once I was in the bay, I felt and succumbed to its force. It swept me to the left, my body a pliant dance partner. Swimming in the other direction, despite the undertow pulling me back, I exerted all my energy to push forward to the spot I was determined to reach.

Only in the water did I feel whole. I had to swim to feel good and had to swim long enough to get lost in the sheer pleasure of moving through the bay. My mind turned to concocting future opportunities in my life that seemed logical while buoyant and much more complicated when I dried off. My body spiraled, flipping over and doing the backstroke, watching the sky. As I swam, the water seeped into my long sleeves like weights wrapped around my arms. It was a challenge, but one I enjoyed, giving me a sense of accomplishment by staying afloat in the movement.

Lost in the timeless zone of stroking, my arms and legs rhythmically moved me further. I alternated from the crawl to the side-stroke, for most people a relaxing movement. For me the intense forward thrust of my right arm targeted the painful contracting scar bands. I felt my muscles loosening, my body lengthening, strengthening, elongating, emerging from the wounds, evolving into something else.

I swam past the Devon Yacht Club. White wooden tables, blue canvas chairs and blue umbrellas covered the white deck. For a moment, I wanted to belong. I wanted to be a golden-tanned blond in a bikini sitting on a canvas chair with a group of friends chatting over drinks. However, I was brunette wearing a long sleeved-leotard, my thighs perpetually white donor sites used to patch the skin on other parts of me. The yacht club fantasy lasted about a minute, replaced by the satisfying exhaustion of my long swim and pleasure of being on the beach alone.

I swam every day for two months. I noticed that my deformed right side unfurled bit by bit. My body, no longer as much of a burden, changed from stiff to fluid, from something alien to myself, to being my vehicle as a swimmer, to becoming a new me.

During that summer, at a restaurant with a visiting friend, I met a man who was training for a triathlon. Bruce and his buddy overheard me talking about my daily swims and assumed we were athletes. Bruce persistently asked me for my number and though I was not ready to date, I gave it to him to avoid explaining why I wouldn't go out with him. My skin was still bright red from third degree burns. The skin grafts made my arm and stomach look like a patchwork quilt. I hid this knowledge from strangers and friends, by camouflaging what lay beneath with silk and cotton loose clothing. I intended to do so for the rest of my life. There was no way I would let anyone else see my body.

Bruce called for a date five times and I said no. On a sweltering Friday night, he called once again. My little cottage felt like an oven. Turning the pages of my book made me sweat.

"Do you want to go out for ice cream?" he asked. I could taste the smooth coldness sliding down my throat.

Sitting in the air-conditioned ice cream parlor, I explained, "I'm sorry I've been avoiding you. I'm not feeling very social this summer since I am recovering from being burned in a fire." I expected him to choke on his cone and quickly take me home. Instead, he looked at me with large sympathetic blue eyes and said, "I would never have known. I'm so glad you survived." My chocolate ice cream melted. Those two supremely kind sentences made me want to spend the rest of my life with him.

Pre-fire, all my boyfriends had been artists, musicians, or adventurers. Bruce was not someone I would have gone out with then. He was a good-natured man ten years my senior, clad in polyester, white patent leather loafers, balding, who worked in corporate sales. We had nothing in common except swimming. For me it was essential for functioning, for him a competitive sport. Yet, it made us both feel more alive. I was smitten. We married a year later.

However, I still wore a long-sleeved leotard for thirteen years— wanting to protect my arm from the sun and my ego from stares I would interpret as pity or horror.

In 1997, Martha, an artist friend, and I gave workshops at an art center in San Sebastian, Spain. In lieu of payment, they covered all our expenses including a hotel on the beach. We had the late afternoons and evenings to ourselves. We could swim in the sea at the end of the day.

I decided it was time to buy a real bathing suit before the trip since no one I knew would see me except Martha, my friend for years and with whom I felt comfortable. I bought a one-piece black number with white piping around the cleavage-exposing top. It was the first bathing suit I purchased since 1980.

I gingerly took off my cover-up. My swim suit was waffle textured, my skin graft arm multi-textured. I held my breath waiting for Martha to mention my scars. Nothing. She and everyone on the beach were looking towards the promenade where a political demonstration about a violent government action was taking place. I realized the inflated importance I had given to my skin's surface.

When we walked into the ocean, I felt the breeze on my arms, and goosebumps as I dangled them in the water. I felt the freedom of lightness swimming unencumbered, propelling me faster to the floating raft. The heat of the day dissipated to cool freedom.

Thirty years after the fire, divorced, I moved to Brooklyn. Much of my life had changed except my swimming ritual. I chose to live across the street from a pool so I could easily engage in the sublime act of submersion and keep my body balanced. Although there are disadvantages to a pool compared to nature's open distances, I appreciated the lack of undertow, year-long accessibility, and unlikelihood of drowning.

I tried to swim at 9:30 every morning, before family time and just after the aquatic rush hour traffic jam when forced to swim in circles. Leisurely, in my own lane, I glided at a continual slow and steady pace until I swam half a mile. Around my tenth lap, I felt my mind's grip loosen on whatever was nagging me. Solutions to problems came and went, as did the problems—each with equal weightlessness.

I was the only one changing in the locker room after my swim. A woman entered. She approached me in my nakedness, ran her finger down my arm, breaching my physical boundary. She said in an indistinguishable accent, "what happened to this?"

"I was burned," I automatically answered. I didn't consider any alternative response to this question asked me countless times over thirty years and always hated the attention.

She just stood there for another minute, then said, "We never know what will happen do we? But you have a normal life?"

"Yes," I replied. I wondered what normal was, but knew I'd worked hard to make the life I had. I breathed a sigh of relief as she left and I finished putting on my clothes.

Boy and Bird Photograph by Wendy Carrus

Jill Ocone
Policy of Non-Discrimination
Poetry

The four-year-old girl
Wearing a pink flowered top
And pink beaded braids
Dances in time
With the hip-hoppish rhyme
And her hips hippy shake.
Her sister leaps in and
Their impromptu recital
Perfectly darling,
A perfect diversion
For all who await
Their treatment today.
The wall is lined
With canes and with walkers
And wheelchairs and crutches
While crosses and yarmulkes
And pentagrams and buddhas
Are worn by
The old and the young,

The toddlers and the grandmothers,
The gendered and the genderless.
There's knitting and sitting
And reading and writing
And texting and posting
And sleeping and talking
And crying and laughing
And eating and drinking
And hugging tight
The green fuzzy dinosaur.
Some absently watch
The garrulous chef
Make pesto from scratch
While others boost
Their earbud volume
To drown her voice out.
There's Carmelo and Brenda
And Ming and Maddie
And Katherine and Jada
And Banjoko and Abdul
And Michael and Shlomo
And Devante and Raj
And Rosita and Ashley
And John and Jane
And Faith and Hope,
All here because
The disease does not discriminate.
The bald, older sister
Of the two dancing girls
Is finished for today
And joins their encore performance,
Wiggling and giggling
And swirling and twirling
Evermore.

Jill Ocone
Nightfall
Poetry

For Glenn

The clock's arms
Tick forward.
The clouds build
Gray and lifeless,
They billow and
Silently explode
Into a
Colorless sunset
As they
Drip with grief
And splintered
Bloodless
Hope.
The shadow
It sneers
From behind
Its sickle.
The sky

It cries
Invisible rainbows
Glittered with
Silver-shining flickers
Of despair.
He dodged bullets
As he fixed
Broken gears
But he could not dodge
This.
Lost.
Nowhere.
I belong to go
No home.
His weeping
It haunts me
While his soft
Gossamer hand
Clasps mine
Tight then
Releases.
His hearty hard laugh
Echoes off the
Barren bookcase.
I don't want to let you go.
I furiously paddle
Still
I fail
To stay afloat
Amid broken bent feathers
And abandoned trinkets,
Dust-covered bottles
And silky-soft
Roses of red

That ride the tide
Out to sea
Alongside
His Soul.

Photograph by Jeff Talarigo

Jill Ocone
Wayward
Poetry

A Sonnet

Sometimes I find myself lost in a maze
Of uncertainty, without direction,
The right way obscured, it's hidden in haze.
I look down and see just my reflection.
I don't know if I should go left or right
Or should I just keep going fast and straight?
Should I slow down, give up, or hold on tight?
The second hand advances...I can't wait.
I take a step forward, and suddenly
I am guided ahead to the right track.
Could it be that now, I am finally
Moving forward with no need to look back?
My soul comes alive and my heart is awake.
My feet are firm. I trust the path I take.

.

Olive Mullet
Water, Water Everywhere
Fiction

For my first solo flight, my husband had just seen me through security—from a distance, of course. I waved to him in my last prolonged view of him.

Then I checked my large purse. No phone. No phone? I am forgetful but surely not that. Only time before I'd done that was at the gym, and handing over their phone, they asked warily if it was a local call.

Now I looked up to see a woman with a child, the child completely forgotten because the mother was checking her phone mail. Another young couple were charging down the thoroughfare, the fellow on his phone laughing. At the gate, just about everyone was on the phone oblivious to their surroundings.

A long-ago dream came to me, having to do with my childhood home. The phone was ringing in that three-story home—upstairs, downstairs. I was hearing it, though I was on the other end. The ringing went on and on, all the while becoming fainter and fainter in that empty house. No contact with my mother, dead these many years, no contact with a house that faded, floating away as though out to sea.

But now in the airport I was looking at the phones in all these people's hands, knowing full well I could ask no one to borrow even for a couple of minutes. Not in these times of distrust, even if I explained my dilemma. Who's this old lady? Couldn't she put something on my phone? Couldn't she charge items on the phone? Theirs was not a public phone. To ask to use their phone would be like asking for their sweater or coat if I were cold.

The highway SOS had long ago disappeared. Do they have anything like that in an airport? I haven't traveled that much but I hadn't seen any phone kiosks.

How would I call an Uber/Lyft to take me to the hotel from the airport? How could I call my husband, until I got to that hotel to tell him of my mistake? I'd lost a lifeline. I could buy a throw-away temporary phone, but hardly worth it for two nights away.

How'd I know I'd feel the need of a phone so much?

My husband offered half-heartedly to FedEx the phone—too short a trip. Of course, I didn't know what lay ahead.

Nothing happened during my stay because I was always with classmates at this 60th reunion of my high school. The day of departure was Palm Sunday, and D.C. was 70 degrees with the red buds all in bloom. When I got to Detroit it was raining, and the TVs were talking of a sudden big snowstorm in the Midwest.

I found the Delta Club and presented my card. No, this was my husband's card and couldn't be accepted. I stammered "but he would've been here, except that he's sick." Sick as in cancer, too tired to travel.

I had managed to get up the escalator hauling the roll-on but when I exited the club on what looked like a platform, the escalator moved like a waterfall going down. Suddenly I found myself collapsed on the floor crying, shaking. A man rushed into the club, and the registration lady came out exclaiming that she knew my flight was delayed and yes, I could come in. The solicitous man was dealing with all Chicago flights being cancelled. I was shaking, aching to talk to my husband or any friendly voice.

Sitting in a corner, head down, I reasoned. Everyone would be too far away to help. How would I get down from this club to get to my flight? I couldn't face the waterfall. The plastic plate with bits of food on it shook so I had to press it against my legs. Finally, I gave up trying to eat, rising to go to the club registration desk again. She was sympathetic while telling me it would be at least another hour before the flight might take off. I told her I couldn't get down that waterfall escalator. I just couldn't. She said, "Oh, but there's an elevator." I hadn't thought of that or seen one. I went back to sniffing in a corner table. I felt crumbled, weak like a baby and yet also felt my age.

Watching the restless, trapped passengers, I realized I was not alone, but they at least were talking to someone who undoubtedly was giving them comfort, soothing words. I had slumped so far forward on my chair that I was slipping out of it when I saw a wheelchair in front of me.

"I didn't order that!" Jolting upright and hot, I had never needed such a thing. I was agile, walked every day. But the young man in front of me did not back away. I remember a less agile friend telling me once that it was the fastest way through the passenger line. We sailed out of the club and swung to the right into a recessed elevator. We whisked around people, such a short time before being abandoned at the gate. I saw no plane nor any person to tell us when it was coming. Like a plane itself circling and circling high above its destination, clouds being the only reality, I felt suspended, lifted into a dream world, not connected to anything or anyone.

Our eventual flight was full of clouds and the landing soft. Clouds morphed into snow all around. It'd been falling for almost twelve hours and was still falling. Winter's muffling and shrouding until we felt the real cold on this spring day. And then through the thicket of moving people I spotted him and we approached closer and closer, he smiling in spite the wintry travail to be on time. Laughing he held up my phone, forgotten when we embraced.

Photograph by Carol MacAllister

William Cass
The Cap
Fiction

Alice heard her ten-year-old son, Luke, come in the back door after school and stop like always at the refrigerator. Some rummaging in the kitchen followed. By the time she got downstairs, he was in his regular position on the living room couch staring at the television, the remote in one hand and the peanut butter jar with a spoon stuck in it in the other. Everything about the scene was familiar except an old blue ballcap he wore; it was worn, faded, and much too big for his head. A faint smell of cleanser wafted in the air.

She said, "Hey, there."

His eyes didn't move from the screen. Alice watched him spoon a glob of peanut butter into his mouth.

"How was school?"

He didn't look at her, but muttered, "Fine, Mom."

She nodded, but he didn't see it.

"Where'd you get the cap?"

He changed channels with the remote and took another mouthful of peanut butter.

A little more loudly, Alice said, "I asked you a question."

"Found it."

"On the way home from school?"

"Yeah."

"Where?"

"Trash can."

Alice felt her eyebrows knit. "It's not sanitary to wear someone else's cap. You could get lice."

"It's fine. I sprayed it with Lysol."

"Still."

He said nothing. She watched him jiggle the leg that he held the remote on.

"It's a ratty old thing," she said, "and too big."

He turned and fixed her with a hard glare, then gazed back at the television. Alice decided to let it go for the time being; she could run the cap through the washer when he wasn't around and try to adjust the snaps on the back to make it tighter.

She went into the kitchen to start getting things ready for dinner. As usual, Luke had tossed his bookbag and sweatshirt on the counter. Alice took the sweatshirt into the back hall and hung it on the coat rack. Her eyes fell on the empty peg her husband had used for his ballcap before his accident, and it was then that she realized the one Luke had found was almost exactly the same. His dad had worn it all the time whenever they played catch, went fishing, or built their model planes together. He'd passed away more than a year before, and still Luke wouldn't speak about it. Her heart clenched and she blew out a long breath. The early spring light outside had already started falling towards gloaming.

Alice waited five minutes or so before returning to the living room and sitting down next to Luke. He made no motion in response. She kissed the top of his head through the cap and inhaled its musty odor. Then they sat silently together looking at the television. After a few moments, he tilted his head so it leaned against her upper arm.

She said, "I love you."

"I know." He paused. "You, too."

Christine Andersen
Downtown after the Mills Closed
Poetry

Along the sidewalk
lined with vacant storefronts

brooms leaning against bare walls,

a row of spinning stools
at the soda fountain
stilled,

the bookstore with
empty shelves and a
plastic garbage pail sitting in the
corner of the linoleum floor,
tiles cracked and missing,

ghosts of chatty shoppers
carrying paper bags with
twine handles
hovering in the doorways
then
as the pewter dusk descends

a spider plant in the window of
Hoagland's Grocery Mart
languishes on
an old cherry table,

its once vibrant,
leggy green leaves
now brittle and brown,

curled like rib bones
around a cobalt plate,

the dried white flowers
that hung in constellations
from its verdant limbs

scattered over the dusty wood
like fallen stars
after the glorious flight.

Photograph by Jeff Talarigo

Marshall Woodward
Love Song #212
Poetry

Me,
A potted plant.
You,
A wandering ant.
Lavender on your lips
from my sunlit charms,
leaves upon your loins
tangled in my dewy arms.
Into my urn you did crawl,
clinging to my roots,
lest you fall.
I licked your ashes,
as you kissed my vase,
remnants of sugary songs
left by some fermenting fruits.
We bitter animals,
circling this sweet maze,
will scatter our remains
in our earthy graves.

Photograph by Jeff Talarigo

Richard Key
The Cure
Fiction

I met Amy at a swanky meet-and-greet arranged by the Phoenix Chamber of Commerce. We all wore name tags. Mine said: *Hello! My name is Phil. I'm with CrystalPure*. CrystalPure is a water filtration system designed for high-end residences. I'm the sales rep for the Mesa/Scottsdale region. Hers said: *Hello! My name is Amy. I'm with The Paper Boutique*. The Paper Boutique is exactly what it sounds like.

The idea was to mingle and exchange business cards over heavy hors d'oeuvres and champagne. Who knows if these things really lead to anything resembling commerce, but something must have prompted the city to renew the event, now in its third year. All I know is Amy was a knockout in this tight-fitting white dress. She looked like one of those models on *The Price Is Right* who smile and gently brush the air hockey table some hyperexcited schmo from Boise is trying to win by guessing which is more expensive, the jar of barbeque sauce or the box of noodles.

We bumped into each other over a tray of miniature quiches. I was planning to sneak five or six onto my plate until she walked up and I limited myself to two. We exchanged business cards as per protocol and each of us explained what we did. I was smoking a cigarette as I tend to

75

do at social gatherings where I don't know many people. We were outside, on the roof terrace of The Museum of Contemporary Art and I didn't think anyone would mind.

"So you care about clean water but not about clean air?" she asked me.

"Of course I care about clean air," I said, taking the cigarette out of my mouth. "See—there's a filter."

"What about my air? I don't have a filter."

"You have to get your own filter."

I thought I was being funny, but Amy thought otherwise and walked over to the next table with the fruit kabobs. If I'd been on my toes I might have asked how many trees were killed in service for The Paper Boutique, but I never think of those things until later. As it was, I was left standing alone feeling like a jerk. Maybe I should have given up there—on Amy, that is, not on the quiches. But she was already starting to take over my brain. I couldn't get her out of my freaking head as I continued grazing around the tables.

I exchanged a few more business cards, had a few more conversations, and refilled my small plate a couple of times. And I must say the fondue was out of this world. What is it about melted cheese? Then, as I was finishing off my last stuffed mushroom, I saw Amy headed for the exit and thought I might get one more chance. I hurried across the floor and slipped into the elevator with her nonchalantly.

"Phil, isn't it?" she said cordially.

"Yes. Amy? With The Paper...uh."

"Boutique."

"Right. Boutique. Listen. I apologize for not being more sensitive earlier. I'm addicted to cigarettes. I've tried everything. You name it— patches, medication, acupuncture..."

"No. No offense taken. I just thought a person who wants to purify water would also be concerned about polluted air."

It was here I wanted to throw out my zinger about if someone is so concerned about the air, they might also be concerned about trees getting killed by the thousands so she could sell delicate stationery to upscale clients. But I held my tongue.

"Say. You wouldn't want to go out sometime would you?" I said.

"Well, you're so sweet to ask. I'm not really interested in starting a relationship right now, though. But thank you."

I could tell she's delivered that line a time or two. The elevator was at the parking deck now and the doors opened.

"Well, I may call you sometime if I have some, uh, paper needs," I said waving her card with my fingers.

"Goodnight," she said, and walked briskly to her car.

Anyone else would have let it go right there, but I have this personality quirk that will not let me stop. I can *not* let a woman reject me so easily. I ended up not far behind her leaving the parking lot and followed her from a distance just to see where she lived. She almost lost me on highway 101, but her baby blue Mazda was easy to spot from behind. Kensington Arms apartments. Nice looking town homes. I only saw her turn in. I didn't follow her all the way to the front door. I'm not some weirdo. Sure, I've had a couple of restraining orders against me in the past, but this was mere curiosity.

My therapist says I have boundary issues. I tend to invade another person's space, she tells me. I tend to make people uncomfortable. I always thought women liked men who were intense. Julie, a girl I dated a few years ago, filed a complaint against me. Said I was stalking her. This was after we broke up. I was merely checking up on her to make sure she was okay. She told the police she was afraid of me. I ran into her at the supermarket—total accident. Unplanned. I asked her if she thought I was a bad person. She said no. She didn't think I was necessarily a bad person, but of all the good people she knew I was near the bottom. How's that for faint praise?

A couple weeks passed and I still had Amy's card in my wallet. Amy VanHoven, proprietress, The Paper Boutique. I still couldn't get her out of my mind, the voice, the eyes, her perfume. That perfume. I've encountered that before—was it Obsession or *Vie Privée*? I found her on Facebook and requested friendship which went unacknowledged. Ditto for LinkedIn. The store had a website that listed her name among two others, but no photographs. Special deals were advertised, such as 20% off all greeting cards on Wednesday.

There were two Paper Boutiques within reasonable driving distance from my condo. I figured she probably hung out at the larger one downtown if she was the "proprietress." I found my card collection was low and thought I might need to take advantage of the discount. And in case you're wondering, it ain't stalking if you buy something.

"Welcome to The Paper Boutique," a voice yelled from the back. It wasn't her voice. I browsed around. Couldn't find a card under ten dollars. People really buy this stuff? Then the bell on the front door jingled and Amy walked in carrying an armful of boxes. I tried not to notice and pulled out a few birthday cards to read. I took one to the counter where she was putting something into a drawer. She looked up and smiled warily.

"Hello again," she said. "Mr...uh...water treatment?"

"Phil," I said. "I told you I might need some cards someday."

"We certainly have some. And you're in luck. Twenty percent off!"

No one else was visible in the store, so I thought I'd go for it as she rang me up on the cash register. "Thought anymore about going out with me?"

"Well, like I said, Phil, I don't really want to date anyone right now, but you're sweet to ask. That'll be $14.25."

"I'll keep asking until you say yes."

"Look, Phil. I don't think I could date a smoker. Quit smoking, and I'll consider going out with you. In fact, I know just the person to help." She reached in her purse and pulled out a business card for George P. Ferris, licensed hypnotist. "Go see this man. He's helped me out with some similar problems before, and I know he's excellent."

"Oh," I said. "All right. So I do this, and you'll go out with me?"

"Do it for your own good, but yes, I'll go out with you after you see George. I'll call him and let him know you're coming."

I waited until the next week to call Mr. Ferris. Dr. Ferris. Whatever he is. I do have an addiction problem—isn't that the first step, admitting it? Any way you slice it, I'm headed for an early grave if I don't cut the habit soon. So far, I've smoked an average of one pack a day for eleven years. Okay—pack and a half, max. That's a lot of nicotine.

I made an appointment and got to pick any day and time like I was some VIP. The Amy effect? So I put it on my calendar: Thursday at 3:00—hypnotist. That sounds weird. Never thought I'd need one of those. *When I clap my hands you will remember nothing.* I wonder if it's really like that.

Thursday at two I exited my office after a conference call with the owners and other sales reps. They announced that I had the highest sales for the first six months of the year. Looks like there's *some* advantage to intensity. I can flat sell things. Maybe customers buy something just to get me out of their hair, but a sale is a sale. I was feeling pretty good. Bonus, baby!

I found my way over to an office building on the east side of town where George P. Ferris had his house of hypnotism. It was on the third floor nestled between a couple of dermatologists and a child psychologist.

Nice little place you got here, Mr./Dr. Ferris I said to myself. *Looks like most of your clients pay their bills.* Never knew there was such a market for high end hypnotism in southern Arizona. And look at this: up-to-date magazines. The receptionist handed me a vibrating disk so I would know when to go to the back. That way they wouldn't have to call out my name. A privacy thing, she said. I was halfway through an article in *People* magazine about Lady Gaga's menagerie when my disk began to vibrate wildly.

George P. Ferris was not at all what I pictured. What I pictured was a Jerry Lewis character with white socks, round glasses, and buck teeth. The actual Mr./Dr. Ferris is a trim 30-something handsome guy with jet black hair and a well-groomed beard. I asked him how he knew Amy, and all he said was they went way back. I spotted a photograph on his desk that looked like the two of them in ski outfits.

I kept waiting for the pocket watch part where he dangles it in front of my face, but he laughed and said that was only in the movies.

There were several items and pictures on the wall, and he asked me to find one that seemed friendly to me. I zeroed in on the sailboat on a lake. Living in the desert, I dream of vacationing on a lake or going to the ocean whenever I can. He told me to close my eyes and focus on the picture. At the count of ten I would be sitting on the boat surrounded by water.

And that's all I remember. I must have blacked out or something. Next thing I knew I was feeling light-headed and saying good-bye to the ladies behind the desk.

Well, call me a non-believer. The only good thing I can say about Dr./Mr. Ferris is he didn't charge me anything. I didn't figure Blue Cross and Blue Shield would pick up the tab, but no one even asked for my insurance card. He said it was free since I was a special friend of Amy's.

But now, two weeks later, my tobacco cravings are as strong as ever. Maybe worse. That quack didn't do one thing for me, honestly. And what's worse, I can't even think of Amy without getting nauseated. Just the name Amy makes me want to puke. I tore up her card into tiny pieces and watched it go down the toilet.

Christine Andersen
Driving on a Rainy Night
Poetry

I worry about the frogs.
They seem to come out in droves
on the wet road
as if there were a plague on

like what happened in Egypt
when Moses wanted out
and got the Israelites set free
to wander toward the Promised Land.

The frogs leap in front of the car
on those springy legs,
webbed feet flying behind them
for lift.

I don't know how many of them I take out.
The whole business deeply disturbs me.

Driving more slowly
seems to inflate the problem,
and swerving doesn't make a difference,
so I press the pedal to the metal,
splashing through the puddles

like a mad woman,
windshield wipers clapping,
hoping my speed will lessen
the blows.

In the morning when I walk my dogs
down the road,
I see the carnage.
Shiny green bodies flattened,
bulging eyes rolled to slits.

If there is a moral to this story,
I can't find one.
If any of those frogs were princes
waiting to be kissed,
they died in disappointment
and the princesses
are somewhere sitting lonely
in their fathers' castles.

When I lie in bed
and listen to the rain,
I whisper to the frogs,
Stay in the woods.
Don't leave the pond.
Adventure isn't all it's
cracked up to be.

But who can stop a frog
from leaping in the rain,
or keep a wanderer tethered
when seeking that second Eden.

Eleanor Windman
Still Michelle
NonFiction

I was anxious and exhausted when I arrived in Jerusalem, and it didn't improve when I took a look at my hotel room. A duplex, with a bedroom and bathroom on the top level; the stairs, floating in space with no risers or handrails, terrified me. I considered sleeping on the living room sofa and limiting my fluid intake.

Dark-green mottled tiles, like silent crocodiles, lurked beneath the surface of the bathroom floor waiting for me to slip up. The Jacuzzi tub-and-shower combo had high sides to scale, a swinging half-glass door to clutch, hot and cold controls unreachable from outside the tub, and a pressure showerhead the size of a pizza that sprayed everywhere.

I unpacked my suitcase. The contents — my usual collection of black Manhattan standard wear: linen pants, tank tops, and short-sleeved white T-shirts. For this trip, my suitcase carried no jeans with giant rips, no cold-shoulder blouses or string bikinis.

I was traveling to my granddaughter Michelle's wedding to a Modern Orthodox young man, Yonaton. As far as I could figure out, Modern Orthodox meant following all the stringent rules of Jewish Orthodoxy, but the men get to show up in jeans. I was wrong. Yonatan is from the Dati Leumi community. They place Zionism at the forefront of their ideology and are more diverse and liberal than most Orthodox Jews. Yonaton did not have a dress code that we had to adhere to.

When Michelle turned 18, she went on Birthright's free ten-day heritage trip to Israel. Something clicked for her. When she graduated college, she joined the Israeli Army, mastering Hebrew, drove an armored personnel carrier known as the Puma, and fell in love with a soldier, Yonaton.

We had always shared our thoughts about life, love, and marriage. We talked about finding a man with the traits she admired in her father and grandfather—my son and my husband. Early on in their relationship, she distanced herself from me. I asked her about it. She took my hand. "I knew how you feel about this choice, and I couldn't risk being influenced by you."

She was right. The enormity of the changes she will have to make in her life frightened me. All the rules and rituals felt like a step back in time for a woman and implied a loss of personal freedom.

I am 82, traveling with my gay daughter, Vicki, her wife, Marilyn, and Vicki's gay son, Ned, from a previous marriage. Ned has lost 30 pounds by counting macros, the amount of fat, protein, and carb grams you eat daily, not the calories. He has recently found love on Tinder. We are meeting up with my younger daughter, Jessica, her Israeli husband, Roni, and their son, Yehuda. He is a college student who studied at a yeshiva for eight years and currently dates a gentile girl from Wisconsin. My oldest grandchild, Max, could not attend; he was baptized a few years ago, but has requested a mezuzah.

I'm used to *mishegas*, but this upcoming event is more complicated than most. I'm swimming in uncharted waters, searching for a glimpse of Michelle's new life, and how that will impact our relationship. I spent a few days before leaving the U.S. watching *Shtisel*— a Netflix series about an Orthodox family living in the modern world— hoping for some insight.

Adding to my angst, Jerusalem was experiencing a heatwave. One hundred and four dusty degrees, the streets littered with construction debris, and somehow all going uphill—a trifecta for my aging body. My grandson holds my hand and walks me to the restaurant the group has chosen for lunch. Trudging uphill on rocky streets, I wail like a petulant toddler, "Are we there yet?"

In the afternoon, I take a long nap and wake up drooling.

Still exhausted, I try to recover enough to sound coherent and attempt to throw off the blanket of matriarchy my son had covered me with before the nap: "Mom, you are here representing the last of your generation." Just what I needed to hear.

Later we are gathered in a family suite, people coming and going, eating and "hydrating." I try to participate and stay relevant, but I ask "What?" so often that I contemplate hearing aids.

I watch Michelle, happy and relaxed, separated from Yonaton for seven days prior to the wedding. They are forbidden from seeing each other during this period of time. I watch her return from the mikvah, the immersion of her soul into pure water, "an awesome experience," she called it. Her long, curly hair falls gently down her shoulders. She is *still* Michelle.

She encourages me to ask her questions, and I do.

"Have you had sex?"

"No, we haven't. It's not allowed before marriage," she sighs.

I wanted to know more about the mikvah, and she explained it to me. "Once you are married, you don't have sex the weeks before and after your period. You go to the mikvah for a ritual cleansing when you stop menstruating. The two weeks a month that are off-limits are spent communicating and working out your life together. I have been taking hormones before the wedding to ensure that I will not have my period on my wedding night."

I don't ask any more questions.

Makeup artists and photographers surround us. Michelle wears a white tulle dress with modest beaded sleeves. The bridesmaids, dressed in pale blush dresses, flitter about kissing, squealing, and reminiscing amidst bottles and tubes of makeup, hair dryers, brushes, and loud music. I peer through a kaleidoscope of youth, as if through a fractured hole, looking for myself. I decide to have my makeup done. "Why not?" I ask. I want to be part of this moment.

As the ceremony opens, the bride sits in a white iron chair bedecked with roses. The bridesmaids stand behind her, her mother by her side. The two fathers, both in navy suits and pink ties, emerge from around a corner and escort the groom to the bride. The tension mounts; the air is filled with sweet perfume. As the groom rounds the corner, he sees the bride and starts weeping and hyperventilating. She sees him and begins to cry. Now everyone is weeping, all engulfed by the couple's passion and restraint. They walk to the chuppah, and a brief ceremony unites them under the canopy.

Wedding at the End of a Tunnel
Photograph by D Ferrara

A party begins. The setting is luminous, a large bell-shaped, curved space, surrounded by ancient limestone walls. Four hundred and seventy souls are dancing, whirling, and twirling to loud, unfamiliar rock music; men with men, women with women, mixed couples, and singles all on fire.

I have to join in this frenzy. The music propels me to the dance floor. I feel no aches or pains, no labored breathing. My children and grandchildren dance with me, laughing and pleased, videotaping me as I dance the Macarena. I'm thinking they are taking a mental snapshot, documenting me—in case I don't wake up the following morning.

At midnight, the music stops. The bride and groom leave, and as she skips away, I look at her. She is *still* Michelle.

After the wedding night, the bride and groom are invited out for seven nights of celebration with their family and friends. The families get to know one another this way, and only after that will the couple leave on their three-month honeymoon. These parties are called Sheva Brachot, seven meals over seven days. At each meal, seven men recite seven blessings accompanied by seven glasses of wine.

On our last night, the Sheva Brachot is hosted by Yonatan's grandparents. Yonatan's grandfather is an esteemed rabbi. I have been instructed not to touch him. They have eight children and 40-plus grandchildren, whom they no longer count since they never come up with the same number. Can you love that many people?

Most of the furniture has been removed and four long tables are lined up in a narrow room, set to feed dozens of people on holidays, celebrations, and Shabbos.

I look around the room; place cards have been thoughtfully arranged by families. I thought mixing it up might have been more effective. Floral centrepieces, made by an aunt, decorate the tables. Three chandeliers, a pair and an odd one, all with fluorescent bulbs, light the room. Bookcases, photos of families, and religious documents arbitrarily hang on the walls. This is a family with something more on their mind than decorating.

Most of the men in the room are rabbis. Their wives, heads wrapped in large, colorful turbans, sit around and yenta during prayers. They are friendly, chipper, welcoming, curious, and Trump supporters; Israel is their only concern. I don't say a word about that.

The newlyweds arrive. Michelle wearing a yellow velvet headband decorated with a giant bow and sequins, her arms covered with a black sweater, her dress resting slightly above her knees. Another giant bow, encrusted with seed pearls, covers the entire top of her sneakers. She is *still* Michelle, but something is different. She is confident about her choice.

Later, Michelle and Yonaton come to say goodnight. They are grinning. She will always be Michelle. We are the ones who must change. *Baruch HaShem.**

> * *Baruch HaShem*   verb
> \bəˈruːk ˈhæʃɪm\ | \buhr-rOOk hAsh-im\
> : Thank God (literally "blessed be the name [of the Lord]")
> **Etymology**
> From Hebrew בָּרוּךְ הַשֵׁם (barúkh hashém), likely via Yiddish ??? השם (borekh hashem).
> An expression used to punctuate most sentences.
>
> The policeman didn't give me a parking ticket, *Baruch HaShem*.
> My grandson is a lawyer, *Baruch HaShem*.

Wendy Lynn Decker
A Djiboutiful Day
NonFiction

     I couldn't have been further from home and still on Planet Earth. A military woman may have been unfazed; however, I was a middle-aged, retired housewife turned civil-servant-professor, and my gig was up. And I was down. Having successfully scored a front seat next to the pilot on an LCAC, the sailors who boarded me, bid me farewell with a sardonic wink and a smile. "It's gonna be a Djiboutiful day." A sense of ill ease consumed me.

     After sitting on a Landing Craft Air Cushion surrounded by tanks, machine guns, and grenade launchers and an escort of military personnel, the final lap of my sixty-day excursion was about to come to a close. I had survived a Tom Sawyer-like adventure, traveled three continents and three countries and now it was going to take three emotionally terrifying days to get home from Djibouti.

     Back on the ship, I'd become friendly with the officers. My departure destination was a frequent topic of discussion amongst other things. It was apparent the Naval officers got a kick out of teasing as well as teaching me. I had also learned not to have expectations when it came to the ship's itinerary. After booking and cancelling a hotel in Paris thinking I'd be departing from France, I tried not to fret, as the change of plans would instead have me saunter into a Cretan hotel and shout *efharisto* as I waved goodbye to the sailors from the Greek island. It wasn't long after that, I realized the Plan of the Day (POD) was exactly *that*, and would change its course on a regular basis. Incidentally, prior to joining the ship as an English Composition Adjunct, I had been warned by other instructors to do my best to avoid leaving from "bad" ports. At the time, I hadn't a clue how I could have any control over that, and the threat of Djibouti hovered in the back of my mind like the stench of a landfill baking in the sun.

"What's Djibouti like?" I once asked the ship's captain.

"It's just like it sounds—JA-BOOTY!" He blurted the way you'd imagine someone referring to the boogieman!

Upon arrival to the first stop toward my destination, my heart raced as the air depleted from the LCAC and flattened out onto the ground. The doors opened and the Marines trampled out first, and I followed carrying my backpack and two large suitcases. Standing on a remote beach on the horn of Africa, danger was everywhere, and I was shaking in my shoes. The stifling 103-degree air weighed down on me as I dragged my luggage onto the gray-pebbled shore. My designer backpack with the gold trim held names, social security numbers, and grades of fifty-six Navy and Marine personnel. It also housed my laptop, which contained all of my personal information as well as my ATM card. Promised a "white van" would be awaiting me, knots began to churn in my stomach like wooden letters inside of a bingo cage. White vans randomly scattered the entire beach, and I hadn't a clue which one was there for me.

Fear and menopausal hormones transformed my body into a human furnace. Sweat seeped from my skin soaking my sleeveless top, pants, and everything in between as I struggled to keep my backpack from slipping. I searched fervently for my ride, presenting driver after driver with a printed email listing my point of contact's name. Finally, one of the drivers invited me inside the air-conditioned vehicle, handed me a bottle of water, and suggested I sit tight.

While doing my best to remain calm, African boys pressed their charcoal faces against the car window vying for my attention. Their naked feet skittered on the hot sand. Narrow pink fingers tapped against the glass soliciting hand-made crafts. I pointed to a small wood carving of a tribal face hanging from a string, cracked the window, and exchanged it for money. Pleading with me to purchase more, the boys mouthed the only English word they seemed to know. Each time, plucking my heartstrings when they said it . . . *Mother*.

Three hours from the moment I disembarked the LCAC which carried me away from the amphibious warfare ship I'd been teaching on, two officers arrived in *the* white van.

"Welcome to Djibouti! Sorry we're late," one of the officers said as he hauled my bags into the other van. "Have you ever been on an African safari?" He asked with excitement.

Intrigued by the prospect as well as his Australian accent, I answered, "Can't say I have."

"Get your camera."

The officers cracked jokes as we bounced over New York City-like potholes and I photographed camel, gerenuks, and East African oryx while we drove across the rocky terrain. After the tour, we reached a paved road where rush hour in Djibouti was no different than the Jersey shore in summertime. The driver suggested I leave my belongings in the van and get to the cafeteria before it closed at 8 p.m.; it was 7:50.

The aroma of garlic, beef sizzling, and pizza wafted through the air. Hungry and tired, I presented the cashier with a military/civilian ID card, which I'd used since day one to access food.

She shook her head. "You can't come in like that."

"Like what?" I asked.

"Your shoulders need to be covered."

I'd already forgotten the rules of the military, so I rushed back to the van and grabbed a sweater from my suitcase.

This time the cashier rolled her eyes. "You need a voucher—or cash."

I politely argued that I had never needed either before, and unfortunately for me, I had given all my money to the African boys. Weak from thirst and hunger, the little girl inside me bit my bottom lip to abstain from releasing a river of tears, then suddenly, I heard someone call my name. In a surreal-like manner, I turned around and the English instructor I had left with from San Diego two months earlier waved me on. He dug inside his pocket, and a minute before 8 p.m. I slapped five bucks on the counter. We shared a meal, swapped war—I mean, teaching—stories and I wished him safe travels on the rest of his journey.

After dinner, I obtained bedding and a key to my sleeping quarters, a.k.a. "the box," another term the sailors had used when describing the lodging accommodations at Camp Lemonnier, Djibouti, where I'd spend one last night on the Navy's dime. Actually a storage pod, "the box" offered more comforts than the stateroom I'd left behind. The room was twice the size and the bed frame contained an actual mattress. Only when the first midnight call to the bathroom woke me, I discovered the facility was about ten pods away from mine. A small bladder won my desperate battle for sleep that night. I could envision the sailors howling with laughter as they omitted the restroom accommodations from the brief explanation about "the box."

Next morning, I prepared to be unescorted and independent in the faraway country. Instructed to hop on a shuttle to the airport, which was only on the other side of base, the major saw no reason to accompany me. Incidentally, because I had entered the country via ship, I didn't have a visa, and I had been pre-warned by several officers that the Djibouti airport officials could make it difficult or impossible for me to jump on that plane. The potential scenario wouldn't let me rest, so I intentionally missed the shuttle and called upon the major one last time.

When I presented my credentials to the stout and rigid dark-eyed airport official, I knew I had made the right decision. Once inside the airport lounge, I collapsed on a seat facing a small bar surrounded by people of every color and ethnicity, but my own. I suppressed my gag reflex from the heavy smoke-filled room mixed with funky scents. Most were as foreign to me as the assortment of people, except for the redolence of body odor.

My friends and family had supported my choice to cut my teeth as an adjunct professor teaching sailors at sea, though a few shared wide-eyed grins and chuckled under their breath. This only invigorated me to prove them I was *even* tougher than they knew. Though I had toughed out 15-foot waves on the Atlantic, fell from a third story rack (bunkbed), and plunged down a ladder well while carrying a box through a scuttle, (luckily using my backpack like a sled), the tough exterior I'd formed was beginning to crack; and I had yet to learn about a Kintsugi mindset.

For the first time, I understood what it was like to be a minority, and I scanned the faces of individuals seeking to connect with someone—someone like me, but I was the only blond-haired, green-eyed female in the room. And each time the voice on the loudspeaker said my connecting flight to Ethiopia would be another hour late, the weight on my chest grew heavier, while the emptiness inside me grew vast. The fear of the domino effect of missing that next flight propagated as each hour passed and I sat in the repugnant airport.

Three hours later, a group of men and women from the U.S. Army turned up. Thrilled to see them, I rushed over and introduced myself, and they offered me a beer. I welcomed the bitter taste, but when it came time to seek a restroom, I regretted having drunk it. A dark stairway greeted me with a cold welcome and an odor akin to a cat's litter box led me to a bathroom with a haggard stall and toilet with no seat (not that I'd sit on one anyway).

Finally, I boarded the flight to Ethiopia, my connecting flight to Frankfurt, which would take me back to the States. Only when I presented my ticket, the attendant informed me that I had indeed missed the flight. I had summoned the *Law of Attraction*. That of what I hoped not to happen, happened. In a maze of confusion, I was shuffled from clerk-to-clerk and line-to-line, like a Claymation character in a stop-motion horror film. With each step, panic gripped me tighter; I couldn't swallow or hear myself think. My heartbeat pulsed in my ear, thumping, throbbing, and drumming. At one point, I stood in the center of the airport gazing around, not knowing where to go. The floor seemed to have suddenly turned sideways, and I was struggling to remain standing.

I forged on, repeating my mantra to another ticket agent. This time, I exchanged a credit card for a visa...an African visa. In addition, the agent handed me a hotel voucher on a white piece of paper listing the address of where I'd be spending the night until my next flight, which would not occur until the following evening at 11:00 p.m. She instructed me to seek the parking lot where I'd find the shuttle that would transport me. I followed the herd of people on the same quest while I kept my ears perked for someone who spoke English. Twenty-four hours in Africa, and I was still looking for a white fucking van. By this time, the temperature had dropped to fifty degrees and rain appeared for the first time in two months. Each time I attempted to share the hotel address scribbled on the white paper, rain blotted out another inked letter. Like the photograph Michael J. Fox carried around in *Back to the Future,* I imagined the paper depleting itself of ink, and I'd be left in an airport parking lot in Ethiopia because my next stop ceased to exist.

For the second time that day, the voice of an English-speaking man with an Australian accent caught my attention. I rushed over to the blue-eyed stranger and showed him the flimsy paper.

"Is this where you are going?" I asked.

"Yes," he confirmed.

"Thank you, so much," I said, my voice weak, but relieved, and slipped in line behind him.

*   *   *

Unlike in the States, no one was buckled in a seat, and there weren't enough seats for everyone. Bent over in a forty-five-degree angle using the handles of my suitcases to balance myself, I took a position near the door. The Australian gazed at me with compassion, stood up, and offered me his seat. Grateful, I accepted, and sat down quickly. Red and green lights flashed before me, highlighting tawdry establishments as the shuttle headed further away from the airport. I tried to dismiss thoughts I was *really* going to be sold into female trafficking or sent to slaughter for my kidneys. No doubt, my coping mechanisms were hard at work keeping me calm. When we finally reached the hotel, I lurched my luggage and myself to the pavement.

Though exhausted, my body was strong from having climbed ladder wells and working out in the gym for two months while on the ship. Not to mention, my adrenaline was on overdrive.

Once again, I stood in line. Now, with a tiny square paper that would prove I had free accommodations provided by the Ethiopian airport for an overnight stay. I approached a man behind a dark mahogany desk with detailed carved etchings. A beautiful painting hung behind him displaying images of men and women presenting burgundy and gold carpets to their king. For a brief moment, I believed my overnight stay might be the plushest thus far on my journey home. With that thought, I took the key, located my room, and opened the door. The result was like being presented with a gilded statue. This time, instead of sweat, tears rushed down my face.

The filthy white couch in the living area resembled what a crime scene might reveal under ultraviolet light. My imagination ran uninhibited to places only nightmares had taken me. With no options, I pulled myself together and dragged all the furniture to blockade the door. One bar left on my phone, and no universal outlet adapter, I sat on the edge of a burnt orange chair and prayed for service as I texted a friend. And like a sunbeam shot from Heaven, he responded, despite the hour of my text. After we hung up, I spread the kimono I had purchased in Singapore across the bedspread, laid a dress over the pillow, and fell asleep.

The next morning, I peeked into the hallway hoping to see someone from the Army or Navy. When I heard someone speaking English, I quickly started a conversation. I shared my story and invited myself to tag along on a trip with the guy and his buddies who planned to head to a mall. A mall in Ethiopia. Prior to that moment, I'd never envisioned Ethiopia in any setting other than a TV commercial seeking support for starving children! Ironically, we spent the next eight hours eating and drinking while we anticipated the next flight toward home.

*　　*　　*

Visa in hand and a friend I'd made from Kenya while in Ethiopia, I stepped on a plane heading to Frankfurt, Germany. Interestingly, my conversation with the Kenyan man had begun when he referred to me as "Trump's People." When I responded, "I'm just an American," he laughed and asked if *I* knew *his* president. At that moment, I realized how sheltered I was as an American.

My flight from Germany to North Carolina went flawlessly, and when I jumped onboard there to catch my last flight back to New Jersey, I made yet another friend. A woman seated next to me happened to live in the same county and we agreed to share a taxi ride home since neither of us had anyone awaiting our arrival. She had cash on hand, but I only had a few Vietnamese dollars and an ATM card. The driver who had found us assured me he'd stop at a convenience store when we reached my town, so I could obtain money to pay the other half of the fare.

The woman and I slid onto the soft leather seats of the black town car. My excitement grew as I got closer to home. Oddly, I felt the same awkward anticipation I once had when arriving home from sleep-away-camp at nine; the notable Jersey shore summer had gone on without me. Nevertheless, I would see my glorious small apartment in just a few minutes, and I would collapse on my full-size memory foam mattress.

The driver pulled into the local convenience store, and I rushed to the machine and inserted my card. A buzzing sound like I'd offered the wrong answer to a question on a game show shouted at me with the words INVALID across the screen! I ripped the card out, wiped the strip on the side of my pants several times, and re-inserted it. However, the same message blared at me again, and then it occurred to me I had told my personal bank I'd be traveling to Europe and maybe Asia; I never mentioned Africa. Just out of my reach, safety and comfort had eluded me once again. This time, I was explaining my misfortune to the driver who glared at me with daggers instead of empathy.

"It's Thursday, and my bank should be open till seven, I said. "It's just around the block."

"It better be open." His voice seemed to have dropped an octave from when he had first smiled and asked if I needed a lift.

We pulled into the parking lot, and I jumped out of the car. The white writing on the window read, *open till 6:00 p.m. on Thursday*. It was 6:15. A man stepped out and opened the door from the vestibule where the bank's ATM stood, and I slipped in behind him. I prayed that my own bank would not reject the card, and I shoved it into the slot, heart pounding, stomach gurgling, barely breathing. My name appeared across the screen, and I practically fell to the floor wanting to praise the machine as if it were God.

"Which way?" the driver blurted. "Left? Right? Come on, this is your town!"

"I'm sorry, I'm just tired—I haven't been here in a couple of months—make a right."

He made a hard right and I flew to the other end of the back seat. Now, *I* was beginning to lose my patience with *him*. Only minutes from home, I forced myself to hold my tongue. Finally, after several wrong turns, we pulled into my driveway, and the driver opened the trunk and handed me the bags. With an unsteady hand, I shoved the key into the lock, pushed the door open, trudged back down the four steps and dragged my bags up and inside and let them fall to the floor. Vanilla and cinnamon still lingered in the air from the candle assortment left on the kitchen counter. I inhaled the sweet scents and peeled the backpack from my shoulders as if it were roadkill I'd carried around like an albatross.

It had taken me three grueling days to get home, and I climbed right into bed and fell asleep immediately, but at 3:00 a.m., I awoke disoriented. When I realized I was home . . . really home, I buried my head into the pillow as if it were Heaven itself. Only hours before I had stood alone on a beach facing the threat of the unknown with a similar fear I had when I boarded that ship to teach for the first time. Eyes closed, I pressed my palm on the Egyptian cotton sheets and swirled it around and grinned. The sailors would have been proud of me, and I knew regardless of the weather, tomorrow would be a *Djiboutiful* day.

Limerick Cat Photograph by Lenore Hart

Sheree La Puma
I Dream of Summer with My Dead Daughter
Poetry

before your wedding.
before the heat of a morning sun
penetrates the cold of skin. before we sit
up top a comforter listening to a
chorus of waves.

before surf unrolls on sand.
before a carpet of blue, grey, & white
beckons us to swim free of wounds,
pressed deep. before divorce robs
you of childhood.

i stroke your curls
with the soft of my hands. make
promises i cannot keep, feast
on the sweet of you,
sacrificed.

today, memories come like bomb

blasts. roots are dying here. let
me weep now. later, i will shed my
mother skin like bark on an old
sycamore.

no longer needed in the dark
nights ahead. i rise with the sun.
we part ways like strangers. i
dream of summer. you grow
new leaves.

Alla Umanskiy
A Story of Friendship
NonFiction

She was a black middle-aged woman from Trinidad, and at first glance, we had nothing in common. Such is often the misfortune of first glance assumptions. Tonya was black. I already said that, but feel it bears repeating. She had short kinky hair and voluminous lips. I am an Eastern European Caucasian woman, pale, blue-eyed. My hair is light brunette (or whatever similar shade my colorist has applied that month) and sadly straight. Visually, we exhibit a striking contrast.

She was a good 10 years my senior, half-way to a different generation, half-way to my mom's age. This also, at first glance, established a divide that is not always easily crossed. She sometimes referenced TV shows I've never heard of or childhood toys that my childhood has never seen. Her kids were roughly 10 years older than my kids, thus in a totally different phase of their lives. She spoke of college admissions, scholarships, their first jobs. My oldest was in middle school.

Then comes geography—Tonya was born in Trinidad and grew up in Brooklyn. She comes from a family of loud, boisterous, animated Trinis; people who go to Caribbean festivals, eat curry and yams, and jam to reggae. We worked together, and Tonya often brought in foods smothered in curry and other spices which made my mouth burn and water at the same time. I was born in Ukraine and raised in Atlanta. My people–Eastern European Jews–eat potatoes and porridges and beef stroganoff. Our music of choice is often a hodgepodge of Euro-American everything, from rock to pop to former Soviet hits.

Such were the generalities that seemingly separated us at first glance. Yet first glances can be joyfully deceiving, because when we both dug deeper, Tonya and I had commonalities that went far beyond the superficial. She spent her childhood in the Jewish Orthodox part of Brooklyn, surrounded by bearded men and by women in wigs ushering their multiple children to private Jewish schools. She came up knowing about many Jewish holidays, having many Jewish friends, enjoying the cuisine of Jewish New Yorkers. When one day I brought in latkes to share, she immediately knew what they were and told me multiple stories about eating dozens of latkes as a kid. Never underestimate the connections that can be made through food!

Speaking of food, Tonya and I had very similar tastes in cuisines. She and I both loved anything Asian, especially small, hole-in-the-wall restaurants which dotted Buford Hwy. (Atlanta's version of Chinatown). We constantly shared our latest culinary discoveries, sending each other links to the grittiest Vietnamese joints each of us could find, which happened to serve the best pho. Like me, she was of the mind that, as she so eloquently put it once, "everything must end with food." When I told her about a family trip to the botanical gardens, she inquired, "Where did you eat lunch?" When I shared that my husband and I saw a movie last weekend, she wanted to know what we had for dinner afterwards. I always smiled to myself: this woman gets me.

Beyond food, we talked for hours about parenting. Tonya was a parent to three children, all of whom she mothered with gusto that would make any Jewish mom proud. Our parenting philosophies and paranoias aligned greatly, and we spent many lunches (over aforementioned Asian food, naturally), discussing teens and technology, peer pressure, choices of extra-curricular activities, and many other issues that keep mothers of all colors and religions up at night.

On the subject of parenting particularly, I connected to her like to no one else. Like me, she worried constantly, about everything. Like me, she tried to be tough, to discipline with consistency, to set the right tone and the right example. Our kids were of different race and faith and age, living seemingly very different lives. Yet, I agreed with her on almost every parenting decision she made, and the way she was raising her brood was very similar to the way I was raising mine. We both tried to walk the line between Tiger-Mothering and helicoptering, between pushing our kids as hard as we could, yet helping them every step of the way—seemingly overused buzzwords in parenting magazine circles, yet also great maxims for the way our generation is raising children. When she showed me the dress her daughter originally picked out for prom, we both immediately agreed that it was too revealing.

When she told me her older son dropped out of college to become a full-time artist, we both, with immigrant blood pulsating in our veins, felt that he should have finished his degree—in art— so he could have something to fall back on. When her middle son, a college athlete in another state, got hurt on the football field and had to be hospitalized, she debated whether she should fly out to see him. I immediately convinced her that there's nothing at work that's as important as her 250-pound linebacker baby. She flew the same day.

I would often show her videos of my kids—drama club performances, dance recitals, swim lessons, baking classes. Her comments were always on point; her daughter was also a dancer; one of her sons had been a drama kid. Our overlaps never ceased to amaze me.

There were other small things that had nothing to do with children. Tonya spoke French; not fluently, but enough to find a bathroom in a French-speaking country, which was pretty much my level of French. We occasionally tossed a few French words around, for fun, and for the thrill of being able to say things others didn't understand. She also spoke conversational Spanish, just enough to be dangerous. Around her, I never felt odd about speaking Russian to my mom on the phone. Multilingualism felt natural to her; like me, she came from a family of immigrants and married into another family of immigrants.

The subject of being an immigrant often carries with it a list of understood rubrics. It takes one to know one, and Tonya and I found each other immediately in this respect. She also grew up with the doctrines of "you must go to college," "you must work hard," "you must select a profession that can sustain you," and, sadly perhaps, "you must marry your own kind." Such are the canons of people who come here from abroad, having to fight for everything they have, having to toil and sweat for a piece of the proverbial American pie. Tonya's family raised her the way my family has raised me; in turn, we were both struggling in certain regards with raising our kids with some, but not all, of these prescribed principles. As such, we both seemed to have agreed on "you must go to college" and "you must choose a profession that will sustain you;" yet we veered from our respective parents on the topic of having to necessarily "marry your own kind," though we both conceded that in some respects that does make life easier. Conversations over Cantonese food on this subject sometimes went on for two hours.

Where is the line that separates people from each other? The line that makes us look at someone and not see them; the line that makes us think, we're more different than alike, we could never be friends, we are not cut from the same cloth. Shame washes over me in waves when I acknowledge my own prejudices and assumptions.

My eight-year-old daughter comes home on the first day of third grade and jubilantly announces that she made a new friend named Shawna. She goes on to describe Shawna, where her desk is, what kind of backpack she has, how they both like math, how they both stay in the after-school program, how Shawna has many braids in her hair. My daughter is super excited–new year, new friend!

My eight-year-old daughter doesn't see color. Not literally, of course– he knows colors. She just doesn't see people in color. She only sees people. I try to follow her lead when talking about her friends, never asking about a person's physical description. What does it matter what someone looks like? My daughter makes no suppositions and has no biases–she just makes friends with whomever she likes, whomever likes math, whomever might sit next to her and share common interests.

"Mama, Shawna also brings a thermos for lunch, like me!" she tells me. Commonalities. Intersection of interests and life experiences and mutual love of math. That's all that matters.

Yesterday, Tonya brought rice and stewed chicken for lunch. I ordered in sushi. We sat in our office breakroom, fluorescent lights overhead, and ate, while discussing the last season of *The Marvelous Mrs. Maisel*. (She's watched it from the very beginning; I only recently binged the whole thing.) Just two coworkers enjoying the lunch hour, while chatting. Suddenly, my phone buzzed. It was my older daughter calling from school. "Mama, I don't feel well," came her small voice over the phone line. For a minute, I hesitated; should I go pick her up? Should I wait until the end of the day? Should I call my husband? I had a presentation later that afternoon, which Tonya knew about—working mom problems. Regardless, she didn't even think twice. "Alla, you need to go pick up your girl," she said, already wrapping up my sushi leftovers. Just like that, decision made. She knew, she understood. This woman gets me, I thought, as I drove away from the office.

Morgan County Still Life Photograph by Patricia Florio

Sheree La Puma
A Mother with Signs of Dementia
Poetry

They say loss is measured in degrees,
in the comings and goings of good &
gentle days. Love beyond reach.
Outside my window, the wind switches,
identities. When Odysseus goes to war,

20 years lost. His story grows without
recognition, more symbol than flesh.
Ithaca forgets. Penelope forgets. Exiled
from self, a series of tests restore dignity.
There are no tests for what Mother forgets,

a poem, a vow, the blue of the sea, vestiges
of the alphabet, minuet in G, minor. My first
steps in white Buster Brown shoes, a wool
coat, locking out solitude. A chill of winter,
but never death. She has lost the ability to

choose her own season. Yet, her fingers still
know the impossible colors of leaves. Together
we exhale, let go of the old moment. It is lost
to us now. She turns & reintroduces herself.
"Hello, I'm Joan." Even with this wound, in

spite of herself, she is mother. Seduced by
whispers she steps into the yard calling
for her children. Noise echoes in her ears.
She searches earth for discarded crumbs.
I join her, empty as a hungry mouth.

Orit Yeret
When Life Gives You Lemons
Fiction

It happened the first time I petted a police horse. I was five years old and my parents and I were on a family vacation in Spain. We were in Madrid, just outside the Royal Palace, and I held my mom's hand as she stared at the city map my dad was holding, both trying to figure out where we were and where we were headed next. Two policemen on horses suddenly surrounded us.

They mumbled some words I didn't understand (I was later told they spoke in Spanish).

One policeman descended from his horse and approached my mom and dad. As they were trying to explain what was going on, in broken language, I let go of my mom's hand when she didn't notice. I came closer to the second policeman, who was sitting on top of his horse and had on these dark shades that sparkled in the afternoon sun. He smiled at me. He asked something.

And though I didn't understand his words, I remember I nodded in approval. He then climbed down from his horse and took my tiny hand in his; he guided me as I caressed the nose of the majestic animal, unafraid, my eyes open wide. With a swift move, he pulled me up and situated me on top of his horse, while continually holding the reins. I remember I giggled. That soft sound made my mom turn around, a look of shock on her face. She grabbed my dad's arm quickly, who, instead of becoming panicked, laughed out loud, pulled up the camera he had around his neck, and snapped a picture.

"So?" Celeste asked as I recounted my memory and held up the framed picture of me, five years old, sitting on top of the Royal Guard's police horse, all smiles. The picture I kept on my bedside table. The picture she had seen a million times.

"So now is the perfect time to adopt a horse!" I exclaimed and placed the picture on the coffee table.

She looked at me, confused. "Adopt a horse?!"

Dear Celeste, my roommate and best friend from high school. Ever since we both got kicked off the track team for calling the coach an *idiot*—which he was—we knew we were meant to be.

I was sitting on the couch in our living room, with my laptop in my lap. Celeste was standing in the hallway. I probably stopped her on her way to the kitchen.

"We have this great backyard we never use; the horse can live there," I replied.

"You think the landlord will approve?" She continued standing there with her arms crossed.

"Why not? He is a...nice...man," I stretched my words.

"Of course he is." Celeste released her arms and let them fly through the air in an over-the-top gesture. "Because that's what we always say about him, 'What a nice man.' Even when he raises our rent every six months and refuses to install proper heating... What a nice man.'" She pushed her palms together, as though she was praying, and bowed with her head.

"It could happen." I tried to remain positive.

"Em, you just got fired, again," Celeste stated and hit straight to my core. She always knows how to get me.

"I read this article about retired police horses. They say they need a good home." I stared at my computer screen, trying to locate the article for her to read.

"*We* need a good home." Celeste looked around our living room, and I did the same thing. It seemed like our exposed brick floor plan did not excite her anymore, though it was the first thing she pointed out before we moved in and continued to refuse we replace it.

"Nothing good will come of it," she said as the kettle shrieked in the kitchen. She hurried then to remove it from the stove.

"Or everything good; consider that," I nearly screamed over the noises she was making in the kitchen.

"Tea?" her voice echoed.

"No, thank you."

Celeste came out of the kitchen with a smoldering cup in her hand. She took a quick whiff, decided it was still too hot, and placed it on the coffee table. She sat next to me on the couch.

"Let's talk about your résumé." She grabbed the computer from my hands and flipped through the documents I had open on the screen. One, evidently, was my résumé.

"Come on." I pulled my legs up on the couch and looked at her. "I've been riding horses my whole life. I *know* horses." My grandparents used to have a big farm upstate and, among other animals, they housed a couple of horses over the years. As a teenager, I would spend entire weekends there, tending to the horses, feeding them, riding them. You could say they sort of cured me. "I want this," I nearly begged. "I've wanted this since I was five years old."

"Four jobs in three years." Celeste did not look at me and instead focused on the screen. "This is going to be a tough sell."

"Sorry we can't all be *career oriented*," I said, using air quotes.

"I'm not asking you to be career oriented, but we do need to pay the bills, Em." She typed some things into a new Word document.

Ever since I met her, Celeste has been very logical and calculated. While I was getting into trouble in school, she was the straight-A student who received prizes and honorary titles from every club she joined. Our teachers could never figure out how we got along—the nerd and the misfit. Somehow, we have always been able to balance each other—the yin and the yang.

But the fact of the matter is—I was there. I was there that day, in the girls' locker room after practice; I was there when she needed me, when that sleazy coach tried to touch her... all hell broke loose. No one believed me. No one believed us.

"Come on." I interfered and pushed her fingers aside. With a quick click I opened up the website I was browsing, which featured some of the most beautiful horses I have ever seen.

"Aren't they cute?" I pointed out the pictures to Celeste as I scrolled down the page. She did not seem amused. "They are all alone in this world, just like me." Celeste still did not react.

"If I'm alone in this world, I need something to pet before I go to sleep," I said, decisively.

"So get a dog," Celeste finally spoke. She placed the laptop back in my lap and reached for her cup of tea.

"No. I'm obsessed with horses." I kept staring at the screen as she sipped slowly.

"Tomorrow," I continued, "I'm going to see a man about a horse, and this time I'm not kidding." I could feel her staring at me, though I did not avert my eyes from the screen. "Come with me if you want, but it's going to happen either way."

Celeste held her cup in her right hand and covered her eyes with her left palm. I looked at her. She was smiling; she obviously wasn't taking me seriously.

"Okay, let me ask you this: What happens when it rains? When it snows?" she said.

"We'll build a shed," I replied.

"We..." she flipped a finger back and forth between the two of us, "will...build...a shed...?"

She spread the words so wide, as if she was trying to give me time to reflect over each of them separately, of how ridiculous they sound, because she has never built a damned thing in her life, not even something simple like an IKEA bookcase.

"I feel like I'm stuck on this couch." I turned my head to look directly into her eyes. "I need something to feel better, be better. It's like it's been in the back of my head my whole life, and all of a sudden it's there, this possibility." I grabbed her arm in excitement.

"Outside thrills are not going to make you happy—you have to look inward." Being a therapist-in-training, Celeste liked to throw that psychobabble she'd tell her patients at me from time to time. I shook my head in disapproval.

"I hate the sad look you have in your eyes, like nothing matters, like your life is empty." She took my hand. "You have a lot and you will have more. Your future is good, Em."

I pulled my hand away from hers. "My future has a horse in it."

"You know...When life gives you lemons, you make lemonade, not adopt a horse," she said.

"Well, guess what, I've been making lemonade my whole life, and it got me nowhere." I reached for the necklace I've had around my neck since I was twelve years old, the necklace my parents gave me as an early birthday gift on a night that changed my life—when a drunk driver hit their car and took them away from me, forever.

"Now, I just want something that I want. Something that I know will make me happy." I let go of the necklace and looked into Celeste's eyes again.

"Don't you want to be brave?" I asked. "Don't you want to take a risk?" I made an effort to smile. "Go for what you really want, without being scared, skydiving without a parachute, just embracing the fall..." I gestured the motion of a slowly falling leaf with my palm. "Because that's what I'm being right now, brave beyond control," I said, triumphantly. "Isn't that the breakthrough you were hoping for?" I nudged Celeste's shoulder.

"Five years in training and I finally help someone," Celeste said, with tears in her eyes. She took a deep breath, put her cup on the coffee table, and wrapped her arm around my shoulders.

"Open up that website again. Let's have another look."

113

Painting by Carol MacAllister

LA Brown
Vondelpark
Fiction

I.

There are three trams that stop beneath Saint Catherine's in Dam Square. Anna and Sam stepped aboard the wrong one, twice. '109 Camelot,' and '113 Shangri-la.' Anna said. The third took them past the museums they'd promised to visit together but hadn't. Stepping off just beyond the Bar Lokaal at the Children's Park, they went through its gate and chose the path that followed the stream. Anna quickened her step 'Shall we pretend to be children, can you skip?'

Sam photographed birds and ducks and things that Anna knew the proper names for: Merganser, Gadwall, and Eider. 'I am still not convinced that a duck is a bird,' he mused. 'I have never seen one in a tree.'

Anna tapped his wrist with her index finger and said, 'You're a dick.'

'I've not heard one sing either.'

They strolled through the park amongst princesses on ponies and fighter pilots swooping in arcs calling 'rata-tat-tat' as they gunned each other down. Birds selected equally cigarette butts and twigs for their nests and paid no attention to either the children or Sam and Anna.

The birch made a low canopy that drew them to a bench by where the stream widened. They smoked and watched the water as it formed an endless undulating quilt over the shallow stream bed. Anna hooked loose strands of hair behind her ear and adjusted her glasses. 'Do you think that your mother will like me?' she asked.

'I hope not, she has terrible taste.'

'We have been smoking too much.'

'Yes, would you like another?'

'Yes.'

'Did I tell you that my mother has tattoos?'

'No, I like her more already.'

'God,' Sam said 'Give me your feet.'

He removed Anna's shoes, then his own, and walked her towards the water with his hands on her shoulders, like he was steering her to a piñata.

'No, you first,' she said.

'Nah,' Sam said, gripping her shoulders tighter.

'Wanker,' she said.

The sunlight reflected so brilliantly that they shaded their eyes. 'It's quite beautiful,' Anna said. Standing mid-stream, the water surrounded them like an organism, funneling around their ankles, splashing and beading on their shins. 'I'd like to stay here forever.'

They waded into slightly deeper water and made motions such that they might come close together, but didn't. 'Did you know that Virginia Woolf filled her coat pockets with stones and drowned herself in a stream?' Anna said.

'Bleak eh?'

'Terrifying. I mean, the image of it.'

'It is something that could only happen in an English winter, I couldn't imagine it in spring.'

'I think it was in March.'

'I'll get my coat.'

'Sometimes I dream of her face staring up at me from

underwater. Not yet dead, but empty like at the end of a scream.'

'Jesus, Anna.'

Anna's mouth formed a curve in the shape of a smile as she bumped Sam with her hip. 'Come on, let's get out of here, I'm getting depressed;' she said.

They walked a few blocks before settling on Café Frans, taking a table on the street. The store windows in Amsterdam mixed sparseness and attention to detail with a selection of tactile and beautiful objects that located the city exactly where it is, precisely halfway between Hamburg and London. Sam and Anna had window shopped walnut tobacco pipes, silver cufflinks, and a brace of floppy leather satchels in one window beside another displaying a singular wedding dress in gold above a floor of dried tulips.

Across from where they sat a street vendor sold pickled herring to a gaggle of old men dressed in linen shirts and blue felt mariners caps. They fed their throats the raw herring by the tail, with their heads flipped back, like hand reared seals. Sam thought that maybe that is what the old Dutchmen were, tame sea lions. Guttural and unintelligible language, visible scars from old wounds, whiskers, sad eyes and a taste for herring.

'They are grandfatherly, aren't they,' Anna said. 'I especially like young grandfathers.'

'Anna.'

'Are you jealous of them?'

'Yes, but it is a pity only in that I have zero interest in young grandmothers.'

'You are wicked. You have probably slept with one but just don't know it.'

Sam laughed, knocking the menu from his lap. Just like the birds, the old sea lions had no interest in Anna and Sam and having been fed they dispersed in ponderous wobbling wades down the sidewalk.

'Let's go and look at that wedding dress we passed.'

'I am not supposed to see it,' Sam said.

'Don't be such a prude.'

'I'll wait for you.'

117

'That isn't any fun. Anyway, you have already seen it.'

'I guess you have a point.'

'We can look together and you can help me get into it.'

'I only need to know how to get you out of it.'

'You aren't doing very well at the moment.'

'Sorry. Let's do it.'

'What?'

'The wedding dress.'

'In high school I remember going to the Homecoming dance. It was the first time that I had worn makeup outside the house. I stood alone the entire night in a paper dress and my mother's coat looking like a dead letter not yet posted. No one spoke to me or asked me to dance. It was awful, dances are awful. We shan't dance at the wedding.'

II.

The lobby of the hotel vibrated with electric light, perfume, and chatter that rang in the evening. Businessmen flowed in and around couples already dressed for dinner and the staff hurried themselves attending to trolleys of luggage and reservations. As Sam waited for Anna he watched a Korean family at the reception desk. The family of a man and woman in their forties and two girls in their teens were leaning in at the counter all talking at once to a clerk who couldn't understand them. The older of the two girls flapped her hand around quickly in an attempt to silence everyone as she concentrated on translating.

The longer the conversation went on the more ill-tempered it became. The man straightened his back, glared at the clerk and started growling in short angry snaps at his daughter. The clerk, frustrated, directed loud exaggerated English in a condescending tone at all of them. The situation became hopeless when the man smacked his hand down on the counter and shouted such that the clerk jumped backwards. The lobby momentarily fell silent. Sam watched the face of the younger girl turn red and saw that her left leg was shaking so much that he though she might fall down.

Just then Anna appeared at Sam's shoulder, 'What's going on?'

'Korean English isn't the same as Dutch English,' Sam said.

'Oh. Did you hear about the airliner that crashed because in Korean there is no polite way to challenge an older person without offending them? Rather than be disrespectful to a senior pilot a junior officer didn't say anything about a mistake that was being made and the plane crashed into a mountain killing everyone.'

'Maybe I'll send my mother to Seoul to get more tattoos.'

'What time are we expected?'

'About an hour.'

Sam had visited his mother's apartment only once before, attending the wake of her second husband two years earlier. He was a diamond merchant and they lived together above his store in the city centre on Kalverstraat. She had stayed on in the apartment and took a modest income from renting out the storefront. When Sam asked her why she didn't consider returning to England her response had been that she felt more at home in a country where the King was queer and euthanasia is legal, like they were in some way connected.

Before going inside Sam and Anna stood on the street smoking. Above them the violet summer sky dissolved into navy promising a starry night. 'It's pretty here isn't it,' Anna said.

The apartment smelled of roast chicken, gravy, and potato fries.

Set around in cabinets and on the hearth were his mother's collection of bric-a-brac and dusty family heirlooms. Opposite the sofa where they sat, on top of a table made from an old sewing machine, pictures of relatives and old pets were set. Sam's grandfather in a home guard uniform holding a rifle, Uncle John and Aunt Mavis, cousin Ben the junkie (before the junk), Adam the Alsatian and Ernie the whippet. Front and centre of the small display was a large photograph of Sam and Emily, his ex-partner, cheek to cheek and smiling. The print and the frame looked new.

Sam's mother didn't walk; rather, she stomped. The wooden floor creaked under the weight of her heavy frame and bare feet. 'Anything you don't eat?' she asked, looking at Anna.

Sam reached to Anna with his left hand and squeezed her knee. 'Anna is vegetarian, I told you that,' he said.

His mother's voice rose quizzically 'You did?' she paused. 'Fries and gravy it is then. I might have a carrot I can shred. I hope you are alright eating out here on your laps, I have just had the table polished. Water?'

'Yes, please,' Anna said.

The expensive wine that Sam and Anna had brought with them had been taken and placed into a side cabinet like it was a gift.

'Can I help in the kitchen?' Anna asked.

'No luv, I'm coping.'

One hour and twelve minutes later they were back on the street. Sam glanced at Anna with a raised eyebrow and tried to read her face. Her expression was that of someone residing a couple of inches behind themselves, like the projection tube of an old television flickering nonsense onto a cracked screen. They started walking back towards the hotel via Damstraat and De Wallen, the red light district.

'I want to see the windows,' Anna said.

'You know that it is impolite to gawk at them.'

'What do they care, they are prostitutes.'

'It is pretty obvious that as a couple we aren't likely to be customers.'

'What do you know about it?'

'Nothing, just that it is rude to stare at them if you are sightseeing and not a customer.'

'Well if they are standing around with their tits out then that is their problem.'

'Why do you even want to see them then?'

'I'm curious. Anyway, I won't stare. I shan't embarrass you.'

They walked through the few narrow lanes of backlit box rooms with glass fronts that remain in De Wallen. Unlike when Sam had visited alone there was no tapping on the glass by the sex workers in an attempt to get his attention. One even turned away when she saw Sam and Anna looking at her.

'It doesn't feel very nice,' Anna said.

'What?'

'Blowjobs for bills behind a window pane, just an inch from the street.'

'They close the blinds,' Sam said.

Anna shuffled through her handbag looking for a cigarette lighter. 'I don't think that I want to go on the canal tour tomorrow,' she said.

'Let's stay in bed all day instead,' Sam replied.

'I don't feel well,' Anna said.

Photograph by Alex Jordan

Alex Jordan
The Swim
Fiction and Photography

I went for a swim in the lake this morning. The water was freezing, but I jumped into it without even thinking. I don't know what took over me; I hadn't done this since my early twenties. It was like a sudden urgency had risen inside me, the urgency to turn an ending into some beginning. So I dived and embraced these contrasting waves, forming around my body and slowly disappearing into the vastness that swallowed me. It felt so cold; as cold as his lips against mine during that final kiss. My husband died last week.

Fifty years. Fifty years building and shaping each other. Fifty years of learning, of caring, ready to fight any struggle that would come our way. And there were many. The doubts, the insecurities. The selfishness and the misunderstandings. We fought them all, striving for that reassuring, gleaming stare that we would exchange once the clouds had blown away. And it was all in there. The curiosity, the liveliness. The humility. All these habits, patiently allowing for some surprises here and there. This complicity, which enabled us to put some of our passion aside and make room for the raising of our children. That same complicity that helped us get it back when they left the nest. It was all in there and no matter what, we knew that together we could take it. Then one day, the coffin about to be nailed, you're found hoping for that stare again as you finally manage to lift yourself from his lips. But nothing happens, and there's no word to describe how brutally it hits you.

I don't know why I went for that swim. Maybe because unable to breathe, I just wouldn't sink either. There was still too much air in my lungs. I can't really say where it came from. My children? It's not like they needed me anymore. They all have families of their own to take care of. But I just wouldn't sink. And then, out of nowhere, it happened. Leaning against the window sill, my mind carried away with some nil as it had been for days, an image unexpectedly popped up in my brain. A sound, rather. That of a young woman, joining her friends in the water and shaking an entire lake with her laugh. Suddenly, as if possessed by some external entity, I grabbed my bathing suit and walked down the small city towards the shore. At the bottom, under this ever-moving surface, many rocks of different sizes were silently resting. They would randomly scintillate and hide in the dark, like the ruins of a majestic edifice left to a floating memory. It was beautiful. Fixed in the sand, the bigger pieces would remain firmly in place, while my feet would agreeably caress the small ones and move them slightly. When I got out of the water, I lay down on the grass and let the sun warm me up. I started to feel a little contraction in the corners of my mouth. I closed my eyes, and I knew that they were shining brightly under their lids.

Ana M. Fores Tamayo
Of Thorn and Bristles
Poetry and Photography

Those letters you wrote me, I imagined
in their green and yellow envelopes wrapped in ribbon
coated red, stacked full, bursting, filled with scribbles, artwork
of our love, our commiseration,
yet ousted into solitary snows of yesteryear.
They remained an elusive memory
of...
No. I will never stain my recollection
of those ink-bled hands with anything of clouded skies,
of darkened bark, of thorn and bristles.
That was not death nor snow nor winter,
not leaves forlorn with autumn's night,
but love's translucent missives echoing in the whispering winds,
a brightened hope eclipsed in words transcending time.

Birds in Snow Photograph by Ana M. Fores Tamayo

Ana M. Fores Tamayo
De espinas y púas

An interpretation, not a translation
(because translation is never poetry)

Las cartas que me escribías, las que imaginaba
en sus sobres verdes y amarillos, envueltas en cintas
revestidas de rojo, repletas de garabatos: notas
de nuestro amor, de nuestra pena,
sin embargo, desterradas a las nieves de antaño.
Permanecieron un recuerdo impreciso
de...
No. Nunca mancharé mis recordatorios
de esas manos – salpicadas de tinta – con cielos cargados,
sombrías costras, espinas y púas.
Eso no fue ni muerte ni nieve ni invierno.
No fueron hojuelas tristes en noche de otoño
sino lúcidas misivas de amor silbando en los susurrantes vientos,
fe iluminada eclipsando palabras que transcienden la eternidad.

Photograph by Jeff Talarigo

Richard Dokey
Velma and Joe
Fiction

Joe went to the doctor. The doctor said it was fourth stage lung cancer. Joe went home and told Velma. Velma broke down. She did not love Joe, and in a year—that's how much Joe had, the doctor said—she would be sixty-three and too old for love.

Joe went into the living room. He sat on the flowered sofa he had taken after his mother's death two years before. Now it all made sense, the heavy snoring Velma complained about, so much so that she had resorted to using ear plugs or sleeping in the front bedroom when it was truly bad; how he could not clear the congestion in his chest, no matter how hard he coughed; the lack of breath sometimes, the lack of energy, the absence of desire—a lavender candle burning in the darkened bedroom to make things romantic, Velma said—as far back as the Tahoe Best Western, where they went for their honeymoon, Velma had burned a lavender candle. It explained the balance problems and why he had installed the hand holds in the bathroom and on the wall for the step down from the kitchen into the den, though there was only one step and the wall was right there. It explained the fright when something quickened inside or something slowed.

Velma came into the living room. She sat in the matching chair

129

from when Joe's mother died.

"Joe," Velma said, "isn't there something to do?"

"No," Joe said, "there's nothing to do."

"But, Joe—?"

He shook his head.

With nothing to do, Velma did not know what to do. Joe was not brave. She was not brave. If she had to cry, she cried when Joe was out of the house. If Joe felt sad or helpless, it was not in Velma's presence. Velma was Velma, and Joe was never any Joe but the Joe she had always known.

Velma watched Joe in the garden, all the parts of him puttering the way Joe always puttered among the roses and stems, but something was there now that was not puttering. In the middle of snipping, arranging or tying off, Joe stopped. Right there, Joe just stopped. He looked at the acacia trees along the back fence. He looked at the amber tree in the Johnson back yard. He looked at the sky, all white-blue, the way the sky always was blue. Velma looked too, holding the curtain back above the kitchen sink. There was nothing to look at. Still, Joe looked.

Then Velma understood that it was not the sky or the liquid amber, all fiery with sunlight in the Johnson back yard. It was just Joe and Joe looking. He frightened her. She had never looked like that at anything.

Velma watched. What did Joe see? Her fright turned to anger because he had made no provision that he might be gone from her while puttering there in the garden. She was forced to a beginning place, where there was nothing to know and nothing to say, so she said, I don't love you, Joe. I never loved you, Joe. I don't want to be in the world with you, Joe. You frighten me. She said these things to herself.

Joe liked to spend time arranging in the garage. He said it took his mind away to arrange the screwdrivers and the wrenches and the pliers and all the things, going across the plywood wall, from the biggest to the smallest. She never touched a thing or asked Joe to put anything where he did not want to put it. It was Joe's place and Joe's tools, and, anyway, she knew nothing about Allen wrenches and Phillips screwdrivers or vice clamps or those pliers you fasten onto something and they stay fastened. She knew nothing of miter boxes or hacksaws or how a claw hammer was different from a ball-peen hammer or why Joe needed so many hammers and things in the first place, like metal creatures in a brood of metal creatures, crawling across the plywood wall, from the biggest to the smallest.

Joe took his tools from the wall and put them at her service whenever she needed this or that done or something repaired. He returned them faithfully, never making a clutter of laziness on the workbench he had built when they first moved into the house. Each time he used his tools he showed her how reliable he was, how he had common sense and she could depend on him.

The garage wall was like her kitchen. The knives were just here in the drawer, the forks and spoons, just there and there. The cups were above the saucers in the oak cabinet to the left of the stove. The glasses were in the next cabinet—the everyday glasses below, the good glasses, for company, above—everything just where everything should be, in clean, polished rows.

There had never been any friction about such things. Velma felt safe and regarded and prepared to render similar courtesies. She took pleasure in putting his socks into the dresser drawer, fresh out of the drier, with his handkerchiefs just there and his Jockey shorts just above them. She laundered his shirts and returned them to the closet, the long sleeves to the left, the short sleeves to the right. She liked looking at the closet floor and Joe's shoes on the floor, freshly shined, the black ones to the left, the brown ones to the right, everything where Joe wanted everything to be.

Now she came into the garage sometimes to use the washing machine, and there Joe would be, standing at the bench, looking at the tools, taking them down, putting them back, making them just so, in their military march from large to small. She was frightened even more. He did not seem to know what to do with the tools except to fuss over them, wiping them with shop rags he kept in a bucket under the bench.

When he was not in the house, she was apprehensive. Maybe he was outside. Maybe he was with the tools. She was afraid to peek out the kitchen window and find him not in the garden. She was afraid to open the kitchen door into the garage and find him, his hands on the counter, looking at the tools but not looking at them. Sometimes he looked at her that way across the roast beef and the mashed potatoes with cream gravy that he liked so much. Velma was terrified.

Joe died. At the cemetery, among the flowers and friends and relatives who could afford to come, Velma listened to the words about dust unto dust and under dust to lie and how a loved one lives on in the memory of those who are loved.

Velma stopped listening. She looked away from the burnished box shining in the sun. She looked across the stones and statues to where the traffic was busy on Sycamore Street. If memory was love, Velma thought, what was there to remember?

She could not remember any Joe but the Joe who lay in the box, a finished Joe, a museum of memory named Joe, like those statues there in the grass, just plain Joe. Their actions, doings and sayings over the years were patterns that became Velma and Joe. Then Joe went away.

At the start, in that funny little motel with the broken sign and the candle whispering in the dark and the scent of lavender and the almost touching of something, she hungered for to be touched, what came was not the clamoring of wings, the carrying down into nothingness, the rise into what she never was but longed to be. What came was being away for a moment and returning to rented sheets, the smell of cigarettes in the furniture and an extinguished candle. And all the years and all the candles had found her where she had always been, and there was Joe, what Joe always was.

What she remembered was that Joe was many smaller Joes, a kind of presentation of Joes, until something emerged into the group, she called Joe. She sorted through these Joes, picking and deciding where they fit and how she could use them.

She remembered how sometimes she caught Joe on the sofa watching her dust. She caught him at the bedroom door, watching her iron his shirts for work. She could just feel him sometimes at the kitchen

132

door into the dining room, watching her mix the peppermint cream cheese frosting for the angel food cake that was his favorite, sometimes behind her when she made the meat sauce for the rigatoni, which, he said, when they sat down to dinner, he could never have enough of, he loved her meat sauce that much. She felt like a girl in a grammar school play.

In making Joe's favorite things and in all the other things, she realized that he gave her the pleasure of discovering what she could do to please him and how he was so grateful for her attentiveness. Joe seemed to know what pleased her and took pleasure in pleasing her. Some essential core remained untouched, that was true, but, looking at the mahogany box, she thought maybe that was because she had always, everywhere, with everyone, felt some essential something in her that was not being touched. How could Joe be to blame for not finding what she could not find herself? Maybe Joe had wandered at the edge of things as well, wondering why there was no proper way to be Joe, like one of his tools, from the big to the small.

She remembered things Joe gave her, little comforts, the weekend projects with cabinets or brick paths out back in the garden, or the redwood planters he made for her azaleas and tulips under the living room window, so that Mrs. Edmonds, across the street, came over to say how she wished her husband Bill was handy that way. The mendings and fixings and carrying of things. The long drives to Salt Lake across the desert to visit her sister Louise. The trips to the Grand Canyon, Hoover Dam, and Yellowstone. All the reservations he took care of. How he kept the Buick tuned so there was never a problem when she wanted it to go shopping. How he told her not to worry about anything because there was insurance. How he took care of all that business when they went to bed.

Things came to her, like pantry shelves being filled when they were empty. She could not keep them from coming. The cardigans he always gave her, Christmas after Christmas, until her dresser drawers were filled with cardigans and she realized that he bought them because it gave him pleasure to buy them, and he wanted her to have one in every color.

Now she understood why she was so terrified when his eyes did not see roses, when his eyes looked at her across the dinner table and did not look at her, eyes that saw something else when he looked at the sofa and the cushions she had arranged or how the light lay on the hardwood floor between the rugs she had vacuumed, when he looked at his tools and did not look at them. The eyes, when they came back to her at the dinner table, were burnings across an immense, dark water, looking at her where she sat in her high-backed chair, drifting as well. Joe's eyes that said that there was no way across to share this thing, that she was drifting, and he was drifting and they were going somewhere, and they were going alone.

Velma wept. The others thought that she had finally succumbed to an irreparable loss, but Velma thought, how horrible it must have been for Joe, how selfish it was of her to be angry. It was her confusion about life without Joe, that was all, but life was all around her. And Joe. Poor Joe. To be abandoned by life and still have roses to prune, tools to keep in order in case she needed something done, shelves to fill when shelves were empty. How terrible to be Joe and not be able to be Joe.

Maybe, over all the years, she was wrong. Maybe it was not wings and falling and a new world. Maybe it was living with someone and finding what someone wanted and giving it.

Ann Christine Tabaka
And Still I Had These Dreams
Poetry

And still, I had these dreams.
Dreams of grandeur, iced in white frosting.
Waking to the truth.
A truth that no longer resides
beside the waterfall of hope.
Reaching for conclusions,
my eyes do not open fully.
Yawning my farewell
to all the glittery trinkets
set forth before the illusion.
A time so long ago,
that memories fail to adhere.
Buried alive in anticipation,
of a tomorrow that will not be.
Sweet songs of triumph
written in the icing,
now melting from neglect.
The night, no longer young,
as I am not.

We join hands in celebration,
the letting go of false intent.
Closed eyes to deep breath,
I succumb to a reality set before me.
And still, I had these dreams.

Ann Christine Tabaka
Swimming Upstream
Poetry

I cannot swim away upstream
with you about my neck.
Some poor lost soul from
a time long before we met.
We are not who we were,
and yet we are who we are.
The weight of disintegrating
dreams, pulling us both down.

The albatross of lore
is here upon my chest,
caged within my ribs.
No battering-ram can set it free.
It has become part of me,
woven into the texture
of my own flesh.
Ripped from my womb,
an apparition, not of my own making.

I wade in knee-deep despair,
searching for absolution.
I sink deeper into the tears
cried out by one and all.
My baptism is complete.
I am released from all false hope,
accepting my penance,
forever swimming upstream.

Barbara Schilling Hurwitz
Birkenstocks and Blazers
Fiction

I checked myself out in the hallway mirror one last time, smiled at the confident face staring back at me and air kissed myself good-bye. "You got this, girl."

I was ready, eager to enter the full-time work force. Today was to be my interview, debut lesson, for the new language arts teaching position at Tall Oaks School. I felt more than confident. I had been substitute teaching for almost a year. And aside from my one lower school experience, I was always happy to be in the classroom.

Lower school teaching awakened an unknown, shameful intolerance in me. Potty talk, runny noses, and small children other than my own crawling into my lap was way outside my comfort zone.

Today I was prepared, dressed in my tan, linen skirt and far too expensive, black and gold striped Ann Taylor knit top. I'd read somewhere to *dress for a position one step above the one you're applying for.* And that I did, right down to my pink leather pumps.

I'm sure I raised a few eyebrows on this progressive school campus trapped in a 1960s-time warp. The frizzy, gray-haired teacher population, male and female, donned oversized, tie-dyed attire and Birkenstocks twelve months of the year, only adding colorful socks to the fashion statement throughout the winter months. They were a physically embracing group, a little too close for my comfort, but I had grown less rigid in their arms and learned to wrap mine around others when enveloped in theirs. They were diehard environmentalists, naturalists, focused on diversity, and they were quilters—none of which I truly identified with. In fact, when asked to join their quilter's club, I had to confess, my knowledge of blankets was limited to machine made down comforters.

I hadn't gone gray yet, and I did use a hair dryer and flat iron to tame my Kramer-from-Seinfeld-like curls. And yes, I'd have to admit if asked, the blush in my cheeks was not natural. But they liked me. They liked my adaptability, flexibility, my humor. I could substitute in any subject area other than math, where my skills remain limited to supermarket addition. And making change is still a challenge.

Today was my day to show off my teaching talent, but as I stood in front of the classroom, an unexpected butterfly migration overwhelmed me, and a trickle of perspiration slipped from my underarm and tickled my side as it rolled into my bra. *Oh God, did I remember to put on deodorant?*

The lesson began with a newspaper scavenger hunt. I had seven pairs of students searching the *Washington Post* headline news, weather forecasts, sports results, comics and obituaries. They attacked the papers like wild dogs for fifteen minutes before I gave the next direction to reassemble their papers.

As they struggle putting their scattered pages and news sections back in order, I introduced my favorite mantra—Organization is the key to success.

The forty-five-minute class was splendid. My underarms dried and my confidence was restored. The observing Middle School Head who sat in the corner watching, smiling, taking copious notes throughout the lesson, invited me back to her office for the follow-up talk.

Yes, I thought, ready to accept my new full-time job, my first since my twenty-year hiatus from the teaching world to raise my four children. While I had dabbled in interior design for years, I continued to hear the classroom calling from the private school sector where I was limited due to my psychology degree rather than teaching certification.

Subbing was the first step, wetting my toes, preparing me for full immersion when I could once again decorate my own classroom, create my own lessons, inspire my own students and take pride in their growth, and mine too. I loved breaking into voices, accents, song and dance, surprising students with my multiple talents while they unknowingly gobbled up grammar rules, built their vocabularies and a love of literature.

Now seated in the Middle School Head's cramped and cluttered office, I pulled my knees to the side so we wouldn't touch. "So," she began without the traditional hug, but with a broad, toothy smile, "wonderful lesson."

"Thanks," *I thought so too. So, let's have it. I got the job, right? I can call my husband and tell him to put the champagne on ice?*

"Well," she said breaking eye contact. My heart quickened for a terrifying moment of uncertainty. "There are a few other candidates interested in the position."

What? A few others? Better than me? Who?

She was still talking while I was trying to figure out who these candidates, as she called them, could be. When she rose and offered me her hand to shake, rather than arms for a hug, I felt like a criminal being released from prison with best wishes from the warden. But I took her hand and said something stupid like, "Guess I'll see you around." And before the automatic door smacked me from behind, I turned and added, "Thank you," which I didn't mean at all.

I needed to run, to get away, go to my car and scream. But Elsie came running toward me, her tie-dyed moo-moo fluttering in the breeze, her cheeks bouncing as she ran to catch up to me. "Wait, so can you sub for me tomorrow? Remember, I have to take my husband for his chemo treatment."

Well, that certainly stopped me in my tracks. I bit the inside of my cheek. *What the hell's the matter with me? So self-absorbed I forgot all about their cancer.* "Sure, Elsie." I could feel my eyes welling and hoped she didn't notice. "Is there anything else I can do? This must be a difficult time for you."

"No, no, we've got this under control. He'll be fine. We'll be fine." She smiled as I wiped a lone tear that slipped from eye. "Oh, and by the way, how did your lesson go today? You know we're all rooting for you."

"Fine...it was fine." I answered refusing to indulge in another self-pity moment. And then I wrapped my arms around her and gave her a big hug, the Tall Oaks kind of hug that offered as much comfort to me as it did to her.

For the next week I waited. Wondered. Teacher friends at Tall Oaks had already leaked who the other applicants were. No one they knew, but one was male, a high priority in this heavily dominated female field, and the other, a woman, a woman of color.

"Shit! I'm never gonna get it. Diversity's a high priority at Tall Oaks." I found myself whining to Ben who has to be the most patient person in the world, but even he was growing weary with me.

He didn't understand. I needed this job. It was matter of pride. For twenty years I'd been a stay-at-home-mom, an also, an appendage on my husband's arm. Too often when being introduced, he was questioned about his career, while I stood by collecting dust mites, grumbling inside, desperately wanting to interject, *and I'm a brain surgeon. Oops, there goes my pager. Gotta run.*

With every passing day my confidence sank deeper, but with Ben's encouragement I busied myself subbing at Regency Park, an all-girls school where I was also in high demand.

The difference between these two schools lead to my closet divide between Birkenstocks and Blazers. Impeccable dress was required at Regency Park. "Preferable but not required" as their rule books stated, "knee-length skirts or dresses, stockings and a blazer no matter the season. Slacks only on the coldest days, but never anything resembling jeans. And never, never any cleavage reveal."

While I wasn't one of the peasant skirt, moo-moo, Birkenstockers of Tall Oaks, I felt more at home there where the motto was Imagine - Explore - Create. Quite the opposite of the rigid ruled Regency Park where debutant decorum was the order.

I had secretly dubbed the principal of the girls' school Mrs. Grundy. She looked and acted just like the principal from the Archie comic books and always appeared when least expected. Her sourpuss and scrawny little body seemed to pop out of lockers, as I passed through hallways. Twirling her long index finger at me, she'd note yet another rule infraction I hadn't addressed.

"Keep your lines straight, ladies. No talking in the hallways, ladies." The girls with more serious infractions, untucked white shirt tails from their blue plaid skirts or, God forbid, polished fingernails, were plucked from the line and sent directly to the office, I feared for a ruler lashing, but was thankful when they returned unscathed.

Imagine my panic when called to Mrs. Grundy's office myself. Had she sniffed out my covered but polished toenails, was my skirt too short or had I slouched at morning meeting?

Ha! None of the above. A ninth-grade history teaching position was opening, and she wanted me for the job. No lesson debut, no other candidates to compete with. Hired today if I was ready to sign.

"Well, thank you," I said still trying to transition from fear to flatter. "I'll have to give that some thought and get back to you."

She stared back, railroad tracks deepening between her brows. "Opportunities like this don't come along very often, Mrs. West. I'm sure you know the high esteem in which our staff is held in this community. Please take your time, but get back to me before the end of the week as I will be forced to publish an advertisement for this position after that."

"Oh, certainly, Mrs. Wilshire, and thank you." I stood and reached out my clammy hand. After a weak disingenuous shake, I thanked her again and left.

My Tall Oaks undercover informant told me the man had bombed the interview. Put his arm around one of the students while explaining directions. *Ew, that's a big no-no. Guess I don't have to worry about that candidate.*

But the woman, the woman of color, seemed to be well

143

received. Rumor had it she'd been the offered the job, but hadn't accepted yet.

I was venting more frustration at Ben that night over cocktails. He sat pretending to listen while focusing on the television news. "I hope she turns down the offer. I mean she can get a job anywhere. Every school's looking for diversity. And who wants to be the token person of color anyway?"

"Oh God, did I really say that?" I stabbed a toothpick into a gefilte fish ball and smothered it with horseradish sauce before popping it into my mouth. My eyes welled not just from the punishing burn scorching my throat and rising up through nose. Between gasps, I managed to squeak out, "Are you listening? This is about my future...my happiness here."

"Right, sorry. Take it easy. Don't give up yet. I think you'll get it."

"You do?" I almost felt relief, like he knew something I didn't.

D-day arrived without word from Tall Oaks. I check my phone for messages one last time. Nothing. I picked up the phone and dialed Regency Park School.

"Hi, Mrs. Wilshire, yes, it's me, Mrs. West." Everyone was so damn formal there while at Tall Oaks everyone went by their first names; faculty, students, parents. I didn't even know their last names. At Regency Park, I didn't know anyone's first name.

"So, can we welcome you to our staff?" she started before I could speak.

"Well, I have another offer," I bit my cheek punishing myself for the lie, then continued, "and I'm considering it as well."

"Oh... And when do you plan on making a decision?" I could hear the surprise in her voice as it raised an octave.

Hmmm, I had to stall. "By the end of next week?" I knew answering the question with a question sounded weak, seeking her mercy. But I was too.

"Well," I could hear her breathing heavily now. "That's too late for me. Our ad will be posted this weekend. If the job is still available when you're ready, I will reconsider you for the position. Thank you for calling and goodbye, Mrs. West."

Ooh, I think I hurt her feelings. But who cares. I don't want to work at that stinkin' school, anyway. I just want the job at Tall Oaks.

Ben came home and found me curled up on the sofa dripping tears into my chardonnay.

"Bad news," he said leaning down to kiss me. "Woman-of-Color accepted the job?"

I laughed at how even he fell into using the moniker. "No, not yet, but I'm sure she will."

"Well let's both drown ourselves in chardonnay then," he said as he poured himself a glass, then dipped the last gefilte fish ball in the horseradish sauce before popping it into his mouth.

My cell phone rang.

I recognized the Tall Oaks number, and chugged the remains of my misery wine before answering.

New Egypt Photograph by Patricia Florio

Charnjit Gill
I Can Kill a Dead Tree
Poetry

There's no rumble in the jungle
There's no "Thrilla in Manila"
Without Ali, this ice cream world is all vanilla
What happened to the murdered rock?
What happened to the injured stone?
What happened to the hospitalised brick?
Unhand lightning
Thunder was realised on bail
Boxing is a business
Ali just happened to give affection and make an appearance
Who would win between the butterfly and bee?
The colours or the honey?
72 rounds
The butterflies don't fly since
There hasn't been a bee that's gone as high since
He was afraid of flying but we haven't looked at the sky since
The world needs some advice since
The advice that he gave, hasn't been applied since
The compassionate kid from Kentucky who became the king of kindness

that's why he wears a crown

He made a lot of requests to the world, but we haven't complied since

Everyone makes predictions but they're not as precise since

The world is in a crisis

Life is just a hyphen

Where heartbreak gave him truth

But love was on his side

If boxing was his cake, then the belts were the icing

Stinging smiles were part of his style for such a divinely inspired man

The courageous knock-out knight that used his knowledge and his knuckles to end conflicts

He hit them where it hurts and where it didn't and made history

He had a political and cultural influence within the ring, but his ability transcended it

He defied impossible odds, overcame obstacles and shook up the world with his dreams

He wasn't bragging when he said that he was special

But is it bragging if it's true?

Confidence, conviction, dedication, giving, respect, spirituality

The greatest fighter of all time was the Ambassador for Peace

His fists set the stage for the struggle

With his Golden Gloves on display

He once said that service is the rent you pay for your seat in heaven

That's why God sent him on a lease

His words were priceless

There is a strength in silence

We remember the times when he was louder than a siren

When he dug his heels in, in defiance

He was always on his feet—floating

But when it was time to go, he bowed his head and raised his hands to the horizon

Travis Cannell
Fifth Gear
Fiction

Three-forty-two in the afternoon on a Sunday, and all was well as I headed into the Sepulveda Pass, hopeful that I might be on time—rare in LA when the 405 freeway is involved.

The distinct sound of a powerful motor snared my attention, and a moment later the gray Porsche came into view—blacked-out windows containing a mystery—and even though the engine didn't change speed, the effect of the Doppler shift was apparent and the pitch dropped as the car flew by, probably at least twenty or thirty miles an hour faster.

A challenge. The pitch continued to drop as the car started to slip away, and I dreamed about who was in this car. After all, this is LA, so probably someone famous, an absolute A-list movie star, and my mind started to conjure images from magazine covers: bright white teeth, flawless skin, and exquisite bone structure, probably a tight dress, low cut with a plunging neckline...And then my car was in fifth gear and the gas pedal hit the floor as I started the chase.

My BMW 540i is a big car manufactured the year before a new model came out, which is a real bonus because BMW takes all of the remaining premium M-series parts and puts them into the next model down on the pecking order, the 540i. So my particular 540i was not a top-of-the-line M series, but did have an M gearbox and several other M items such as the M interior trim and a beautiful, big, shiny metal M on the steering wheel. To the non-BMW enthusiast, I could claim my car was an M, and although this particular machine certainly was not, and clearly stated 540i on the bumper, once inside, the M on the steering wheel did the convincing. "See—it's an M," I'd say with a smile as I rubbed the shiny metal M, and my passenger would nod her head in agreement. But the M gearbox was real—geared low for fast acceleration—and the gearbox had something I'd never experienced before: six forward gears.

Granted, the sixth gear was just for gas conservation and absolute top speeds, but the magical extra gear created room to transform fifth gear into my new favorite gear. Fifth gear in the 540i on the highway had seemingly unlimited amounts of power to accelerate. Fifth gear was the solid rocket boosters strapped onto the space shuttle. Fifth caused all the passengers in the car to reach for the handle as they gasped. Fifth was why I loved the 540i.

Traffic was light, and over the course of the pass, I was able to catch up to the mystery but only close enough to follow, not close enough to pass or pull up alongside for a glimpse at the Academy Award-winning young actress who was gunning the engine, tempting me, beckoning me to give chase.

I see the Porsche picking up speed on the downslope after the pass and merging right toward the 101 southbound, which was good because that is where I, too, was heading. I got into the middle lane with the mystery on my left and punched the throttle, hoping to pass before the on-ramp, but the Porsche also picked up speed, and the closest I get was front bumper to back bumper, the angle not good enough for me to see inside. Then, ahead, I see my lane was slowing down, so I braked softly and fell in line behind, keeping the car in fifth, matching speed, and looking for an opportunity to pass as I heard the singsong whine of the Porsche. Through the back window I glimpsed the outline of a small passenger, which made no sense. How could this young beautiful actress have a child? Younger brother?

We merged to the far left on the 101, but there was no way I could pass, so I started to look for an opportunity to get in front, or at least to the side so I could see inside and know. I had to know.

I saw an opening in the far right, two lanes over where the traffic was thin. I downshifted into fourth as I maneuvered the car over and punched the pedal—pushing the RPMs of the engine higher and higher, almost into the yellow. Cars in the middle lane whizzed by like puffs coming from a gun, the Doppler shift strong, thirty or forty miles an hour at least. The Porsche picked up still more speed, but then I was in fifth going all out, and for the first time I got neck and neck with the gray Porsche, and in between the cars blinking by in the middle lane, I could see inside:

The man in his fifties, maybe sixties, hair gray with typical lines of male pattern baldness. Wearing a suit without a tie, shirt unbuttoned in a way that told a story, buttons ripped off? Then I saw the young boy in the right seat staring forward, hands on legs, back ramrod straight. The Porsche hit a bump, flew up in a giant bounce, and the kid lost his body image: arms swung wild while hands grabbed the side of the door—hanging—then back to the previous position, holding himself together from the inside of his being, tough.

Now the right lane slowed, and I was too close to the car in front, so I braked hard, then harder, and the car lurched forward as the suspension compressed and the seat belt grabbed me. A passenger would have screamed. Shoulder check, downshift, then merge to the middle lane, and for a second there was a crack of opportunity where I could pass the Porsche, get ahead of it all, and look into my rearview and see, really see and know who was driving and who that child was and why they were pushing 120 on the 405 at four in the afternoon on a Sunday. But then a yellow Volvo merged from the left lane in front of me, and I had to make a sudden decision; my turnoff was coming up on the right—Coldwater Canyon—and the Porsche was going faster and faster on the far left: exit now, I'd be on time, or chase the Porsche to get an end to the story, because after all, this is LA—everyone loves a good story, even if you're late. But maybe I'd just follow them to some house in Pasadena and never really know anything other than the look of terror on that child's face when the car jumped and the way the man's shirt was unbuttoned...

Better to be on time.

Cynthia Singerman
Gold of a Fool
Fiction

We stared together at the magical snow globes, the glitter and white swirling around the miniature cities and bridges. You said you would buy me one. But you forgot.

Or maybe you didn't forget. Maybe you remembered, but you never had a chance to give it to me, because we only met once more. Only that one time, when I took a seventy-dollar cab I couldn't afford, to a club by the beach. And you kissed me in front of your friends and your sisters. And I was so happy because it felt so right, and that's why it hurt so much in the end, because I had been so wrong.

And you were gone.

I almost bought you an apron once. I forgot to tell you that. You would have worn it long after we were through. Years later, after you had filed me away like a postcard of a place you visited once, you would still be wearing the apron to make your famous pasta.

And the air would smell of garlic and tomatoes, sweet and sharp. A tangy block of Parmesan cheese on the table. Every flute and fork turned gold with your Midas touch. Although when I look close enough, there is a hint of green. Because I know now, it is the gold of a fool, a plated charm.

But your teeth still shine like pearls, iridescent in the candlelight, never turning purple from the Chianti. *Veneers.*

"A little coffee stained," you had said. We were at breakfast and it was raining outside because it was always raining or drizzling or *wet.* The streets were slick with a consistent sheen of precipitation.

"What?"

"Your teeth."

You do not blink. I blink though. Your eyes are the same color as mine. Sage tinged with gold, a startling shade of hazel. They say people are attracted to similarity. And we are similar, but we are too different in the end. I do not know this yet. Or I do, but I want to fight against what I know with every fiber of my being.

"What about my teeth?"

I smile widely because you had told me once how much you loved my smile. But my throat catches, a lump of molten hot marble, made of doubt and fear, cracking my neck in two.

"They are a little coffee stained. Yellow. You should bleach them."

I trace my dry swollen tongue over the enamel. We had gone out the night before and I'm still wearing my black miniskirt and tights. There is a run on the calf and I can see my pale skin through the tear. I draw my finger up my leg, dragging it over the ripped material, not knowing what to say. I am unraveling. I am coming undone.

I buy a new camel coat and a scarf the color of bubble gum. I didn't dress in all black anymore. Color. Lots of color, like a peacock. You told me this one night, when I wore a dress with feathers and fishnet tights that looked like flesh. *Such a peacock.* And you shake your head and I want to ask you what you are thinking, but I'm too afraid to know. Always afraid that the next words will be you're leaving. I need you to stay.

We text each other on pay-by-the-minute Motorola phones. I press the buttons, watching the block letters the color of steel appear on a faded yellow screen, my heart bursting through my mouth in one beating, bloody eruption every time you respond. And you always respond.

I've never felt this way. I want to tell you this, but I swallow my love only to choke on it. The repressed emotions leak out of me in unfortunate ways. Your words wake the flow of fear, all my insecurities that rested as a dormant disease before we met. And we speed towards a brick wall. But I don't pump the brakes. I downshift and press the accelerator waiting for impact.

We had met on a hot summer evening. My dress was short, and I made a comment about the fine wine you weren't drinking. A line from a movie I knew impressed boys because I was good at that, quoting movies, being funny in my little black dress. My skin was the color of saffron- colored olives from the day outside, and my perfume smelled like red fruit and caramel.

"People are watching," you had said. "I don't like being watched." And you took my hand and we ran. That should have been a warning. Not being seen. Not being known. Alleys and basements are not places for love—it's too dark and everything dies without light. Nothing grows out of cement.

We took the tequila shots, I remember, letting the heat scald our chests, lighting us up before chasing it all down with the sweet limes on our lips. There was this steam, this thick air that followed us and we were alone on the dance floor, sharing a kiss that took my breath away.

"Come over," you said. An invitation. Finally.

And I walked the straight path from my tiny room above a clothing shop, passing the theater announcing *Joseph and the Amazing Technicolor Dreamcoat*. I would walk this path a thousand times. A million times. Always the same sign with a rainbow-colored cloak, vibrating on a black and white backdrop, always the man wearing the magical jacket. This is why I remember, after all these years, what play they were performing on the stage, while I was on my way for you to break my heart.

Photograph by Lenore Hart

Lenore Hart
Hypatia in the Library
Poetry

Tonight the moon is eclipsed by a dark cloud. One cannot measure what can't be seen, though scholars will always try. But no astrolabe I've built can measure the distance between opposing minds. The stars gaze down on us but they never reveal why the ignorant revel in their state, burning books and scrolls instead of reading them. In nature flames are clean. They clear off brambles, the dead wood that hinders growth. Embers glow, subside, then cool. Ashes feed the next generation. Men bow before a stone, or cut and cross two sticks to thrust before them, making religion a shield against knowledge. But faith which shuns science is not wisdom, denying our place in the cosmos.

An unlucky star steered my birth to a time when triple turmoil
roiled the narrow minds of three religions. My father schooled me for
mathematics, not martyrdom. In the lecture hall I clothed myself in
chastity, fending off groping hands and heated looks, for virginity is the
only currency a woman may coin in the marketplace. Despite the laws
my reach exceeded a grasp of washbasin and cauldron, the amphora and
spoon placed in a girl's hands in lieu of learning.

I tried to escape into numbers, which hold more beauty and promise than the material world. Plato would agree: reality is an ugly curtain which spoils the looks of any room. I built astrolabes to measure time, the sun and stars. But no forged-brass tool can reveal how to navigate the shoals between a safe life and a certain death. My students were men who flocked to hear me speak, no monks or bishops among them. Rabbis and clergy railed at the notion of a woman in lecturer's robes, a female who dared worship human intellect instead of a god. They gutted the pagans, leaving only two faiths to fight it out: Christian and Jew. They razed my holy place, Bibliotheca Alexandrina. No church or temple or field of standing stones, but the greatest library ever built by men.

I need no astronomer's tool, now, to see the mob approach, their hatred blessed by a bishop. The monks are armed with sharpened shells and tiles. My skin prickles with the knowledge of our parting. The names of gods come and go. But the mind, I tell myself, perseveres. So come: flay my skin. Burn my limbs. Blades can penetrate no deeper. Your fury, a hot but empty desert wind, releases me to walk among stars I have named. In future years the world will speak of me. While your corpses rot unknown, in unmarked graves, bones shrouded in delusion. This knowledge is the only cloak fine enough to pull around my shoulders when I rise to face the murdering mob.

Hypatia, born around 370 CE, was in her time the world's leading mathematician and astronomer, the only woman for whom such a claim can be made. She was a popular teacher and lecturer on philosophical topics, attracting loyal students and large audiences. Her philosophy was Neoplatonist, deemed "pagan" during an era of bitter religious conflicts. In 415 CE she was murdered by a mob of monks, who reportedly flayed her alive, inflamed by the hate-filled sermons of their leader, Cyril. He was the Bishop of Alexandria, a contentious theologian who closed many churches down and drove the Jews from Alexandria. For these dubious achievements, the Roman Catholic Church canonized him in 1882.

Lenore Hart
*Looking Into the Eyes of a Woman I Must Tell
She's a Writer*
Poetry

Your gaze rises to mine across a neat stack of pages
scored like a flagellant's back by my red pen. A wry,
jaunty smile fails to conceal the hope in your eyes.
This moment always feels like a mild seismic shift
that only affects two: Each a pillar which might fall.
One has been here many times. One is only hopeful,
despite the show of diffidence, that she's created
work that will change her life. And oh yes, it will.
Hold onto this moment, then, a little longer.
For afterward, when I've told all the truth, everything
will change. Though for the most part in ways
you have not yet even imagined. Innocence:
That is you, now, in this exciting moment of
recognition. But that second is always too brief.
Then it's gone. Of course, you will face more times
of truth and recognition: the first contract. The first editor.
The first words on a published page. Later these will
be balanced by other truths which are even now

waiting in the wings for their cue to rush on stage:
The harsh rejections. The savage critics. Readers who leave
nasty comments and few stars. Once it's set in motion
you can't get this breathless, heady moment back. Time
goes on, until comes the morning you no longer want to see
your own face reflected in a computer screen. When
you look away, down at the keyboard, hands simply
resting there, with no idea of what to do, which keys
to strike, what words must be formed next. That too
may only last a moment. But it has you now, this lifetime
prison you longed for, back when you only knew how
wonderful words made you feel, with no idea that
they had the power to hurt you as well, so very badly,
in ways you had not yet even dreamed of.

Patricia A. Florio
Celebration
NonFiction

Every year, we celebrate my daughter Kristin's birthday at a wine tasting event, held at a big old park in New Egypt, New Jersey, that houses the winery. We've been attending this festival every November for ten years.

My daughter is a generous person. With us, she also invites two other couples with their children. Food vendors sell ethnic dishes, including ice cream and desserts. It's a joyful, fun day for everyone.

Last November, Kristin made a dramatic offer.

My husband had gone through two forms of cancer over the past eight years, with chemotherapy treatments and three surgeries. We've piled up expenses to the point of not being able to pay our mortgage and property taxes—taxes that have tripled since we moved into our home twenty years ago.

Kristin has always been daddy's little girl, sensitive to her father's feelings. "Move in with me and Amelia," she suggested. Amelia is our twelve-year-old granddaughter, the child we have had with us since the day of her birth.

At first, I couldn't conceive of selling my house. It was my home! My friends were near. My writing events were centered in that town; as were the things that made me happiest: looking out at the ocean every morning, listening to the waves lull me to sleep at night.

Could this work? Moving in with her? Kristin is the youngest of four, with three older brothers. Growing up, she was a trailblazer, but outspoken. I wasn't sure I wanted to go through the nasty mouth syndrome again as I had during her teenage years. Not that I don't say exactly what's on my mind. But did I really need a sparring partner at this age?

Kristin has always made tough decisions for herself, like having a child in her thirties and not getting married. Again, Kristin was committed. She was going to relieve her father's burdens despite me.

In February 2020, we moved in with her. We have our own bedroom on the first level – I even got to paint and decorate as I wanted. My husband has hope again and feels better about life. If not experiencing mindless bliss, Kristin and I co-exist (mostly) peacefully. From a life spent thinking "Father Knows Best," I've come to realize that daughters know a thing or two also.

I'm looking forward to this November—sitting around the firepit, having a glass of wine, feeling warm and blessed. Having weathered some of life's challenges: not heartbroken about the things I had to give up, I appreciate the things I have.

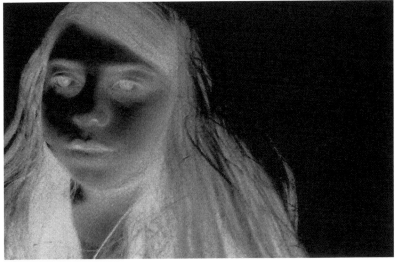

Amelia Exposed by Amelia Hope Florio

Cindy Waszak Geary
For the Love of Delphiniums
NonFiction

"My mother's favorite flowers were delphiniums," my 93-year old mother told me one day last summer. Before this revelation, I would have thought my grandmother Ethel's favorite flowers were the blazing red and yellow tulips that, every spring, lined the stone path leading to her front porch—Dutch flowers for her Dutch ancestors. When I mentioned the delphiniums to a cousin, she confirmed what Mother told me. My cousin had heard the same thing from her father, Mother's younger brother. I find it a lovely thing when tidbits of surprising information from Mother's childhood bubble up into the middle of conversations with her, conversations otherwise fraught by dementia's grip on her mind and memory.

Mother continued with her story, "Your grandmother grew the most beautiful flowers in Haywood County [North Carolina], and the most beautiful of these were her delphiniums. People vacationing in Waynesville for the cool mountain summer would drive out to the country to buy Mother's delphiniums because they heard hers were the best. Everyone knew. She could talk to people from town and from out of town. She was a smart woman, and she knew how to grow the most beautiful flowers."

My grandmother and granddaddy grew up poor in the Appalachian Mountains of North Carolina; before the Great Depression my grandfather had been able to support his family by selling and repairing Singer sewing machines, but he lost this means of livelihood when the bottom fell out. During the worst of it, he dug up stumps and sold them for firewood at ten cents a truckload. Eventually the family was able to make enough money to survive as truck farmers, and even after the Depression they continued to support themselves by raising bedding plants for other farmers. Mother was the second daughter of four in her family—with two brothers, one at either end of the birth order. She and her siblings grew up knowing long days in the fields and hunger at night. The fear of not having enough has stayed with Mother all her life, as it has for many from her generation.

By the time I was born in 1955, my grandparents had managed to see all their children in college and almost all of them married. Granddaddy was able set up a new shop in town where he got back to selling sewing machines—now Pfaff machines. They still grew food for themselves. They always had a garden—a big one—which provided food in season and for canning and freezing for the winter months.

As I thought about Mother's story, I imagined my grandmother comfortably talking to people she did not know about something she cared about, something she had grown and loved. She didn't suffer fools—or foolish grandchildren—but she was kind. And of course, being the Southerner she was, she always was polite. There was a softness around her; she put people at ease. I imagine her coming in from the field or out the back door from the kitchen of their white wood-framed farmhouse when she heard a car come up the gravel driveway. She'd be wearing a faded shirtwaist dress with an apron over it and low-heeled pumps caked with red-clay from the garden. She'd take time to make sure the people who drove out for her flowers got to pick out the ones they wanted. She would cradle their bunch of cut flowers in the crook of her arm after she cut them. These 'not from around here people' would maybe get a glass of sweet tea while she tied the flowers in a bouquet.

Delphiniums (also called larkspur, but not by my mother) are grand, regal flowers, each tall stalk with ladders of five-petaled lush, almost lavender blue blossoms that can be lighter or darker depending on the variety. I found photographs of them after Mother's surprising disclosure, and I thought they'd be lovely in the sunny area on the side of my new house. Their color would dazzle against the neutral gray siding. I began a plan to grow some myself, thinking through what I would need to do. More than just an aesthetic addition to the landscape, I wanted to grow them to honor this ancestor, my grandmother—now more than four decades after her passing—a grandmother whose connection to my life, I lately had been learning through photographs and old letters, was stronger than I had known it as a child.

To get this project started, I ordered delphinium seeds from an online seed store. I had hoped they grew from bulbs—that seems easier to me—but they grow from small, dark, shiny seeds. I have put in the extra work in the past to start other flowers from seed, so I knew I just needed to do what I needed to do, planting them in small containers with starter soil, keeping them in the garage so they'd be in the cooler darkness they needed for germination.

I thought, also, that growing my own delphiniums might please my mother—pleasing my mother no easy task ever—a lifelong struggle, in fact—and now complicated with her dementia. Whereas my mother felt lost in a big family, I was her one and only for five years before my brother was born. The pressure to make her happy in the midst of her 1950s-style housewife isolation made me think that I alone controlled her well-being—an unfair burden for a child and a hard thing to unlearn emotionally as an adult, even as I began to understand rationally that that idea was crazymaking. But we here were again, because of Mother's dementia, in this old familiar place. No other blood kin around to help, so who else is there to make her happy?

Mother's suffering is intense and it hurts my soul to think about it. She is embarrassed when she cannot remember things; she also is scared and paranoid and lonely. She forgets that my father died a decade ago and thinks he is not around because he left her for friend D_____. She experiences grief every time she finds out he died, which seems like about 50 times a day. Painful memories her conscious mind locked down for good reason surface as obsessive thoughts of anger and shame. Yes, there also are moments of light—like when she thinks about her mother's bright blue flowers—but they are too few to justify the rest of the horror show. There is nothing good about dementia. I am glad for people who have a gift for working with people with this condition. I am not one of them. I have learned lessons from it, but lessons not worth the pain of it.

But still, in spite of this, maybe because of this, I strive to do something, anything, to make it better. Illogically, those of us left in the wake of this disease try to imagine what would give a rational person (like us!) a moment of joy. Without remembering that the whole problem is not remembering, and because happy memories make us happy, we look for ways to spark memories that will make our loved ones happy.

But there is the catch—it is almost impossible to orchestrate a happy memory. Yes, the memory of Grandmother's delphiniums came from Mother's mind—several times—but only at the bidding of the incomprehensible workings of her dementia-diseased brain. At any particular moment without any identifiable reason, my mother may not be able to concentrate on what I am saying to her, she may be in an unhappy delusion of my father criticizing her for spending too much money, or she may be focused on why I wore a red shirt that morning.

More than once lately, I have walked into her room as she was still awake inside a dream of Christmas at her mother's house. Each time she asked me if I'd seen who was downstairs, if the guests were still there, and why I was not dressed up for Christmas dinner. This dream makes her as happy as I ever see her, but it is ephemeral—and I have nothing to do with this effect—except to not tell her it is a delusion. Because really, I'm open to her reality being her reality. She's communing with people I can't see. If it makes her happy, I don't really care whether the thin veil between this world and some other one is a metaphysical experience or a metaphorical way of understanding what his happening in her brain. She believes it; it is true.

Thus, growing delphiniums in an effort to elicit mother's pleasant memories of her mother is most likely more about trying to make myself feel better about trying to please her than it may actually please her—my complicated reality. But

Delphinium Photograph by Cindy Waszak Geary

inspiration comes from where it comes from; it seems almost impossible for any of us to make it happen, try as we might. For anyone who has attempted in some rational, linear way to create something or make something happen—most of the time you can get just so far and then it feels like there is a brick wall in your path.

Until....until all of a sudden, when you see the first delphinium seedling come up through the dirt and eureka! you know that your grandmother is whispering in your ear! She asks, "You want some relief from your mother's gut-wrenching, soul-sucking dementia? Want to know more about me than you could understand while you were a child?" She tells me, "Get your hands in the dirt and enjoy growing and nurturing these beautiful flowers! Find the joy of sharing them with others. Take some to your mother when they bloom. Maybe they will make her happy and maybe they won't, but their beauty will make you happy and others who see them. And while I'm giving you advice (young lady!)—get yourself to the mountains and see the kin you have left there—and bring some of those beautiful blue flowers to the Greenhill Cemetery for your granddaddy and me."

And several days later, more seedlings shoot through the soil. I feel my grandmother smile in my heart.

Marian Kaplun Shapiro
Over Your Head
Poetry

Before you learn to swim
remember that you are not a fish
or a turtle, or even a dog, or a duck
Don't go over your head
even with your water wings,
firmly hugging you, and be sure
the lifeguard is paying attention to you
(not to that cell phone or that cute kid
showing off in the shallow end).
Sometimes it's good to be afraid
of riptides and undertows, of lightning
and hurricanes. Of jellyfish and sharks.
It will be many years before you know
when you are safe
to be out of your depth.

Photograph by Carol MacAllister

Tommy Vollman
The Truth or Something Like It
NonFiction

    I met Joe Nuxhall a few weeks after my fifteenth birthday. His hands were gnarled, and he spoke as though his mouth was half full of marbles, but he was sharp and funny as hell. I was only a few months younger than he was when he made his Major League debut.

    At just 15, Joe Nuxhall climbed on the hill at Crosley Field in the top of the ninth against the would-be World Champion St. Louis Cardinals. Manager Bill McKechnie called on Nuxhall with the Cincinnati Reds on the short end of a 13-0 deficit. Nuxhall's debut was essentially mop-up duty at Niagara Falls.

    Still, the Ol' Lefthander managed to retire two of the first three batters he faced before all hell broke loose. Nuxhall never finished that half-inning; he never found a third out. In fact following his debut, it would take him eight years to get back to the Major Leagues.

    When I met Nuxhall, he was half of the radio broadcast team for the Cincinnati Reds. I shook his hand and asked him to sign a baseball card my uncle gave me years before. The card was a 1963 Topps. On the front, Nuxhall was framed in mid wind-up, his arms stretched high over his head, his throwing hand hidden inside a chocolate-brown mitt. The back of the card was jammed with stats. When I first received the card, I wondered if the 67.50 ERA listed for 1944 —his rookie campaign—was a misprint.

I was enamored with that statistic. The pitchers I knew of in the bigs had ERAs in the 3s; the really good ones were in the 2s or below. For a long time, I was sure my Nuxhall card was simply a misprint. No pitcher, anywhere, at any time could possibly, I thought, have had a 67.50 earned run average.

But Joe Nuxhall did.

67.50 was no misprint.

Nuxhall was a legend. He was a good pitcher—great, even—a Cincinnati Reds Hall-of-Famer who won 135 games in his 16-season big league career. His lifetime ERA—3.90—was a far cry from the ultra-inflated number of 1944.

While he was signing my card, I asked him what it was like to face the St. Louis Cardinals at age 15.

He stopped his Sharpie mid-signature and stared at me. The room we were in—a large, partitioned conference room at the downtown Westin on Fountain Square—seemed to go silent. A wide smile cracked across his face, and all the air came back into the room. He adjusted the thick, wire-framed, aviator-style glasses that perched themselves on the bridge of his nose and leaned back in his chair.

"You know," he said, "I was so goddamned nervous when I got the call, I tripped and fell on the way out of the dugout."

He leaned forward, his elbows on the white, cotton tablecloth. His eyes grew clearer, even more focused. He seemed to stare not at me but through me.

"I was used to throwing to good hitters, even some really good ones," he added. "But," he continued, "there's a difference between a good hitter and a Major League hitter. I got two of three, then gave up a walk."

He shook his head and smiled.

"I was there, up in the hill, and I look over and see Stan Musial in the on-deck circle. Next thing I know, he's up at the plate."

He leaned back again in his chair and stretched his hands over his head in nearly the same way he had in the photo on my baseball card.

"Then," he chuckled, "they scored some runs. Lotsa runs."

His smile was so real, so sincere, I'd have believed anything and everything he said.

"It wasn't that bad," I replied. "Only five."

Even to this day, I'm not sure why I said what I did. I'm not sure what I was thinking. At the time, when I heard those words tumble out of my mouth I could hardly believe I'd said them. I thought Joe Nuxhall might punch me in the face.

But he didn't punch me in the face.

Joe Nuxhall was too much of a class act for that sort of thing. In fact, what he did left me as awestruck as anything has since that time.

Joe Nuxhall leaned toward me, his hands flat, fingers spread, and said, "Son, they could've scored as many runs on me that day as they wanted."

He handed my card back to me, his signature split in two segments, and nodded to the person behind me.

As I stepped away, Nuxhall spoke again.

"Hey kid," he said. "Thanks for that."

I smiled and nodded, puzzled as to why in the world Joe Nuxhall would thank me for reminding him of his horrendous Major League debut.

As I got older, I think I grew to understand why Joe Nuxhall might've thanked me. Now, I'm almost sure of it. He thanked me because I gave him a chance to be honest when it would have been so easy to be dishonest.

I wouldn't have been honest as Nuxhall.

I couldn't have been; I care too much about what other people think of me. More accurately, I care far too much about what I think other people think of me.

Which often puts me in quite a bind relative to the truth.

It shouldn't, but it does.

Now that I have kids, I'm more conscious (or at least I try to be) of my issues with truth. But old habits die hard, and it's still far too easy for a lie to slide off my tongue. Most of them are harmless—nearly all of them are, really.

At least that's what I tell myself.

The truth, of course, is that none of them are harmless; all of them are lies, and all of them are aimed at deception. All of them evoke pain and erode trust. All of them—every single one of them—are destructive, cancerous, corrosive.

Which is exactly the opposite of what I tell myself.

I wonder what Joe Nuxhall told himself. I wonder how it could have been so different from what I tell myself. I wonder if Joe Nuxhall ever considered anything but that truthful, face-up story about his big league debut. I wonder if Joe Nuxhall ever offered any excuses, ever messed around with the size or shape or structure of things.

I'm sure he did.

Or at least I'm sure that he considered it.

But I think he figured everyone knew the truth already. And even if they didn't, he did, so what difference did it really make? What happened, happened, and Nuxhall's honesty may just have freed some space for other things, things not destructive, corrosive, and cancerous. Nuxhall's honesty helped him get back to even. And eventually, he got ahead.

I want to free some space. I want to get back to even. I dream about getting ahead.

Lies are heavy, clumsy, and awkward. Lies are unruly; they're contradictions. Lies are a misguided effort to reconfigure the space-time continuum. They're an attempt to overwrite history, to highjack experience, to gaslight and usurp. Lies are an essential impossibility, yet I try to execute them day after day after day. Some days, I even manage to convince myself I've successfully executed them. Of course, that's a lie, too.

I'm not really sure when or why I started lying. I know it had something to do with power. Control, too. My lies offered me a mechanism for getting what I wanted, what I thought I needed. They gave me agency, and as inauthentic as that agency was, it sure as hell felt good, so the lies grew.

I think I finally understand why it was so easy for Joe Nuxhall to be honest. Being honest is really the only possible—the only sustainable—outcome.

It took Joe Nuxhall eight years to get back to the big leagues after those five earned runs in two-thirds of an inning. Eight years. And the weight of those five runs is nothing compared to the weight of the lies I've told.

The weight of those five runs cost Joe Nuxhall eight years; it took him that long to get back to even. I wonder how long it'll take me to get back to even. I wonder if it's even possible.

Photograph by Jeff Talarigo

Thomas Penn Johnson
Really Drunk?
Fiction

There's a newspaper report that last Friday evening a forty-eight year old Liberty Township resident was pulled over by a Sheriff's officer for recklessly swerving on a yellow moped. The investigative halt was anything but routine. When the officer went back to his squad car to run the man's name, the man took off and ran. The officer threatened to release his police dog and the man responded, "Do you want to die?"

The dog caught up to the man and chomped down on his right leg, but the man kept running. In the ensuing melee the man continually shouted "Do you want to fucking die?" while attempting repeatedly to grab the officer's handgun, and eventually he disarmed the officer.

After another minute of struggling the officer succeeded in handcuffing the man, who shortly thereafter apologized for the incident claiming he didn't remember reaching for the officer's gun or shouting "Do you want to die?" because he was "really drunk." The man was taken to the hospital where he needed surgery for dog-bite related injuries, though he told the doctors, "I don't care about that leg, just get me a beer." The man's blood-alcohol concentration was measured at 0.26.

Even while reading the story many readers were struck with the similarity of this arrest to the arrest a year or so ago of another Liberty Township man, a forty-nine-year-old, who was charged with disarming a law enforcement officer, battery to two policemen, resisting arrest and disorderly conduct. Police had gone to that man's Liberty Township home to enforce a court order to commit him and the man came at the police with his fists. Setting aside what mug shots might reveal about the two men, the two reported arrests were interpreted by 'most everybody as what they superficially seemed to be—unrelated bizarre and violent official encounters between police and two addled-brain citizens whose minds were flustered by spirits of one kind or another.

But one reader, a Shamanist more than a thousand miles away, who happened to know each defendant, immediately suspected that there was more to this than meets the eye—that these two incidents were related in that spirits and spiritual forces were indeed involved in both. He was well acquainted with the spiritual struggles that had tormented the forty-nine-year-old since youth. He was certain that the man on the yellow moped was adept at communing with spirits, including the spirits of his ancestors and sundry opportunistic spirits who could happen upon him through customary or preternatural means. After thirty years separation from each, he owned proof still that each man had loved him when each was sixteen years old, though neither was aware of the love of the other.

Most people are acquainted with only fictional characters that are fully cognizant of their magical powers and thus can wield them to produce dazzling feats of wizardry—characters like Merlin, Faust, and Obi-Wan Kenobi. Though they may not be entirely dismissive of the possibility of the existence of the Nether World of Invisible Spirits, most people have never witnessed actions they would attribute with certainty to invisible spirits. Such a one is the forty-eight-year-old who protests he does not remember details of what happened when he was "really drunk." To this the distant reader can well attest, for he observed that phenomenon thirty years prior.

It was at a time when the distant reader was learning by strange demonstrations to believe in powerful invisible forces. His first encounter was with a new-found friend who exhibited a propensity to swoon when they would get together on weekends. And woe-betide!, they discovered, any sensitive soul who physically came between them when they were become interlocutors

One evening this friend snorted some dope and swooned into a comatose state in which he ceased to breathe. Afraid for his friend's life the man was forced to intervene with mouth-to-mouth resuscitation, and he discovered forthwith as they shared in breathing that the both of them were become transformed into one knowing carnal being.

Thereafter, the man realized he had the power to enter comas near or far, a fact he verified twice—once with a man nearby he had never met, and once with a man he knew who was miles away. Thereafter, he was also surprised to discover that he could be seduced and enthralled by a similar means of mouth-to-mouth resuscitation. And also, thereafter, he learned he could use a storm to carry his thoughts to summon a friend who was far away.

But yet more remarkably he watched a boy drink a single shot of whiskey and immediately vault from his seated position into the air, somersault inexplicably, and land on his back no longer fully conscious. He gathered up the barely ambulatory boy and ushered him slowly to his car and drove towards the boy's house. During the ride the boy did not speak or open his eyes. When the car was parked the boy's eyes remained shut, but he extended one arm and began to speak. He spoke fluently in what sounded like the dead language of some long-extinct American Indian tribe. He did this for ten minutes.

Astonished, but silent, the listener sitting behind the steering-wheel waited for an opportune pause to lean over and speak into the boy's ear: "Whose language are you speaking?" With eyes still closed the boy replied: "Mine."

The next day the youth did not remember anything that happened in the hour following the moment he swallowed the shot of whiskey, so his friend decided it was his duty to inform the boy of all the details because it might well be dangerous for the potency of this ominous knowledge to be kept secret from the boy. It proved, however, injudicious not to consider that the boy was too young to prudently assay the import of such knowledge, of being told only once of such things— the gravity of imbibing spirits, susceptibility to trance, the lifelong need for a congenial friend and spirit guide, traditional ancestral obligations and the burdens of being a chosen one who is the keeper of a language. For thirty years the one who could not remember what spirits did to him simply lost his way and often ran amok.

The forty-nine-year-old was a "pretty boy" when he was a young man. So extraordinary was he that his peers, especially the women, did not resist openly complimenting him about his stunningly long, golden blond hair and other distinctive body parts; and often one would remark to another, "You can see he doesn't belong here!" Easily provoked to envy the boys nevertheless respected his manliness and, curiously, were afraid to make him cry, which he would do if you stole from him or broke his heart.

He began his tussle with demons at an early age, so practically had no choice but to reckon with their existence and act in self-defense. His parents' marriage gone bad drove him to run away from home when he turned fourteen; retrieved, he ran away again at sixteen; retrieved again, he was sent away to a prep school but eventually he took his schooling into his own hands and found his own tutor, and he moved out on his own when he was eighteen. While yet a teenager he dumped his teenage girlfriend for her mother, an affair most mature and satisfying to both lovers; a teenager still he took up also with a wily streetwise vixen who was anything but an honest whore.

Thanks to his tutor, he got his high school diploma by correspondence courses, and thanks to his grandfather he went to work for the county at age nineteen and never had another job. But in order to manage a turbulent marriage to a violent stripper, a tyrannical father whom his mother divorced, other familial stresses including the loss of his tutor friend, as well as occasional emotional breakdowns and hospitalizations the man needed to defend his *psyche* with the severity of an anchorite. His ally and refuge for these last fifteen years has been devout worship in evangelical Christian religion. He severed ties with everything that had come before he was saved and thus for him the demons are held at bay, more or less.

Seeking to bring secret truths to light when one is old is difficult and even dangerous. It was under the cover of darkness that the Pharisee Nicodemus sought out him who he believed was a teacher come from God. As also did The Grand Inquisitor in *The Brothers Karamazov* conduct interrogation. The difficulty for Nicodemus was hindsight, not foresight—to lift the veil through which he viewed his former days, to abandon the darkened prism through which theretofore he had viewed his life. He asked the question that any old man imprisoned in darkness must eventually ask: "How can a man be born when he is old; can he enter a second time into his mother's womb, and be born? How can these things be?" Most any man would just as soon be left alone to live his life as he was wont.

Before being placed in his own individual cell the forty-eight-year-old in the county lock-up was transferred from the infirmary to the weekend holding area where two repeat offenders were being held. He knew one of the men, and that was Danny who, the same age as he, was a former schoolmate. Danny was a town drunkard known to the police for thievery; he was a nice enough fellow who had taken to living on the streets when he was a teenager and having never found a permanent residence or a permanent job he had eked out a bare subsistence by his meager wits and very good looks which by neglect were now long gone.

The other older fellow the dog-bitten inmate did not know by sight, so he asked him outright: "What are you in for? They got me for being really drunk. Ten High."

"Trespassing, like always," replied the scruffy-looking man wearing a well-worn poncho and a very old necklace made of deer bones strung with hide. The man turned away, obviously preferring not to talk.

Danny explained, "The hoity-toity folks out at Long Lake don't appreciate us low-lifes wandering the grounds of their new mansions. It ain't like it was when you and me used to go swimming out there back in the day. There was a time you went anywhere out there you wanted and the cops couldn't find you if they hunted for you all night. Course, I ain't been swimming in Long Lake since we was kids, and I wouldn't go out there now 'cause the rich new folks done hired them private cops to keep us regular people out. Course Indian here, he don't pay nobody no never mind."

"So!" says the forty-eight-year-old speaking to the older man, "You are the one they call 'Indian'! I been hearing about you my whole life, never knew whether to believe what people say or not."

"People call me Indian."

"You don't look much like no Indian to me."

"POTAWATOMI."

"So how come you been hanging out at Long Lake for all these years?"

Danny speaks up: "Why, Indian here is the groundskeeper. Leastwise, that's what people say."

Looking away, as though talking to himself, Indian says: "Ancient burial mounds. POTAWATOMI must always walk the grounds, speak to the Earth, and bathe in the water. POTAWATOMI must listen to voices of the spirits, must hold conversations with the trees."

Drawn into nostalgia by Indian's reverie the forty-eight-year-old wistfully recalls: "This tree I knew beside a full ravine used to talk to me when I went swimming out there. I had this friend who sometimes talked to other trees, and he would say that I should speak and take no thought to be no one but me."

Danny's recollection is stirred: "A black dude? I remember him. I used to swim with him out there. Crazy dude, used to talk to trees and wind and birds. Wrote poetry. I remember him, best friend I ever had before he moved away. Whatever happened to him?"

Indian answers, "It does not matter where he is, his spirit is remembered at the Lake."

Danny's nostalgia turns to melancholy: "Those were good days when we went swimming. A lot of wasted days since then. Too bad, can't turn the clock back now."

"Resetting the clock is not the same as turning it back. The waters wash us every day we bathe." Indian's words, Danny feels, would shake a poltroon's soul; Danny is struck dumb.

Three deputies arrive to escort the injured moped driver to a single cell, so Indian questions urgently: "You say you knew a tree who talked to you?"

The forty-eight-year-old replies: "Well, it made noises, seemed like to me, so I made noises back. It was one of those weeping trees. Why? Does it talk to you?"

"It never talks to me. No one else has told me that it talks. The spirits say it pines for one who speaks the original Anishinaabe language which POTAWATOMI no longer knows."

The deputies lead the prisoner out, so Indian speaks forth wisdom-words to the departing prisoner: "From now on you would be wise to do all your drinking with that tree!"

Looking back over his shoulder, the prisoner responds: "And why is that?" To which Indian calls out: "Do you want to fucking die?"

Golden Gate Bridge Photograph by Judy L. Mandel

Lisa Bledsoe
Blue Crawfish
Poetry

i.

There are crawfish in our seep the color
of Chagall's sapphire skies, his birds and angels—
the color of amazement and unexpected flight

The stream breathes them gently;
in the dictionary of infinite life
bubbles rise from beneath blue swimmerets,
enchantment gleams along each carapace,
each spreading cobalt tailfan—

the best time to see them is in the rain,
or on the fringes of the lavender dark

ii.

She teases her delicate way
over stones and disintegrating grasses
over leaf letters written to sky—
her antennae turning up rumors
of green promise unfolding
on the other side of the planet

But for now she swims amid drifting
flakes of mica, beneath the red flags
of staghorn sumac that still burn
above the icy water and swiftly cooling mud;
her claws folding autumn goldlight into lengths
and tying knots in the weeds for memory

iii.
You still have a chance to fly, little sister
—to take wing and join a painted
sky filled with sea, with bouquets
pressed to a bride's heart, and
the sound of violins and moonfish—
all blue, all indigo and flowing azure

The bridges are swimming in mist;
come before the snow sails
and be filled and finned with wind and
feathers, and never before heard songs

for blue dreams of love.

Lisa Bledsoe
Benediction
Poetry

Where her fingers touch the forest floor of my skin
a spark spits white, a stinging point goes in.
Soon my scalp prickles with a circlet of embers
flickering in the weald; I have become
will-o-wisp: there is treasure in the fen
        if it can be uncovered

The kindled light of needles has fetched
my awareness to a thrumming in my head—
I slip up the pathway and am suddenly
astonished to find a tribe of cloud-foot people
        dancing in a round

Respectfully I ask (because I do not
know, despite being in my own body)
        what—
this company is doing
dancing in the high henge of me and
without stopping
they respond:
        calling down blessing
I have some experience speaking with those

few others see, but this time I retreat
to the sanctuary of my secret breath
to consider, turning this over in my hands
like a bone etched in extraordinary sign

The rhythm continues above
Steprise, pulseflow in pattern
            —a shape I do not know
but what I do: acknowledge
I am filled with *benedictus*, a spirit-fairing
            and for this I give thanks and linger
there, my body a glyph, a map of lights,
a well of fire and juice

Needles spark and sing as they leave
their chaplet, and I remember to ask before
the communion fades: what can I do to help?

and hear, as I return to the dusky room,
to the woman unlocking the map of energy
in racing threads on my body:
            keep the circle open
            this is where your healing lives

Alex Jordan
Il Campiello de la Pescaria

Fiction and Photography

It's one of those moments when everything seems so removed from you. Your body. Your thoughts. Every gesture that you do. Her. You bring the cigarette that you rolled absentmindedly to your lips, and the smoke that comes out, already turning into the nil that you breath involuntarily, like a gentle disappearance, reminds you that no haven can last. There's only time itself and its enduring. Its rigidity and yet absurd, uncontrollable changefulness.

And now, it seems to have stopped altogether, letting you hang in your own introspection, your own doubts, your self-anonymity. Your lack of understanding, like a knife stuck in your stomach and spinning very slowly, replacing the tired watch lying patiently on your wrist. The emotion, even the pain, feels so distant, too. You can't write them down, or at least not yet. Time has stopped indeed; all you can do is trace it back and maybe you'll get it going again.

You leave your recently renovated flat and start walking, walking for hours or maybe just a few minutes. You can't really tell. You proceed mechanically, each step slightly more aimless than the last, without knowing where you are heading. Until you pass that empty square that makes you halt suddenly. You haven't seen it or even thought about it

189

since you were a kid. You had actually forgotten it was there. It hasn't changed. Il Campiello de la Pescaria. So empty, and so full of these memories that you thought you had lost. But they had been there all along. They had stayed in that little square, untouched and as strong as ever. All these silly games you would come up with, joined by the other kids from the neighbourhood.

The world you would create in your head, and the stories you would make up along for your friends to enact, some dubiously first but always amused in the end. This theatre of yours that had no stage, no spectators, and no rules. And when short of imagination, all these football games, or the water bombs during the summer. All these cheers, so

Photograph by Alex Jordan

loud and irreverent, each of them like it was the first and last time that you would ever laugh. How far and yet so close it feels now. How many years has it been exactly? The place looks colder and smaller than it used to. It doesn't belong to you any longer. You need it more than ever, and perhaps that's the irony of it all. You can't make it a world; it won't let you. Only a memory, so many memories, and an emptiness as insignificant as the passing of your shadowed silhouette. You resume your walking, in the vague hope for a new deserted square around the next corner, one you could make your own. All you will find is some paving stones to roam upon silently, and in each of them, the remote sounds of unrestrained happiness from a past that you can't touch. You know it all too well, but what else is there to do?

Right then, however, as you are about to enter another narrow street and leave that square behind you, you notice something. It's hard to say what. You stop again. Is it the decay on the walls and the ground you are standing on? Their insalubrity, which hasn't changed either. It was always there. Or is it the darkness of the place, too small and the houses too high to let in the rays of that burning sun in the sky? Or is it just a memory?

That of a kid, sitting in a corner early in the morning, the place so quiet and devoid of life. Struggling to find new stories that would make them all leave the confinement of these walls, of their daily life, and let them fly away from that dirty ground and touch this bloody sun they were deprived of. The boundless curiosity of that kid, and his secret determination to discover new places to be reimagined as he pleased. The inner sensation that he didn't belong to this square, that he was only passing, like a silhouette eager to be filled with any source of light that would come his way, and with it, the shadows that it created as well. All the little paradoxes that surrounded them and which he couldn't help but marvel at. Their comforting melancholy and a solitude that would never leave him.

But above all, the bursts of joy, of passion and of love that they would throw in the air, like a piece of freedom to be shouted and to be shared and to be kissed, like a beautiful doubt, through every smile and every tear, through every impression left behind to a place or somebody's face, a celebration with no beginning and without an end, the celebration of a child and of a man, of their eternal dance and of the music that would always play in their head. Among the silence of the empty square, a repetitive noise, almost imperceptible, drew your attention. It came from your watch, marking every second that went by. You got up from that corner and started walking towards his recently renovated flat, each step like one of these seconds, like a minute or an entire day to be lost, but ironically, like a memory to be lived.

Alexandra Dane
Found. Well.
NonFiction

I check into the Hotel La Fête on a white-hot June day missing my ovaries, a tumor, appendix, one third of my lymph nodes, two feet of colon, my gallbladder and a riverbed of gallstones. I trail behind the *madame*, my suitcase wheels sinking into the seams of the mossy walkway, feeling every one of those thirty-six surgery incisions. At the bottom of a stone spiral staircase the innkeeper slaps a large key into my palm, gestures upwards and dismisses me with a sharp *d'accord!* Pivoting on her high heels, she sashays away.

Last November I decided—in spite of the cliché—to make a bucket list after the three cancer-driven surgeries over thirteen months. At the top of the page I wrote: *workshop in Provence*. I needed an incentive; the diagnosis and procedures had stunned me immobile. I had an oncologist, night terrors and was completely dependent on my dog and family to function. My life had tunneled down into scarce meals and bed at 8:30 every night.

On Christmas morning the last package in my stocking revealed a small clay pot of *herbs de Provence* and a note curled up inside that read,
You are signed up. Love, your family.
Six months later and a continent away I lift my foot to attempt

the first step — all of seven inches wide — and my sweaty hand slides off the iron rail. I halt with one shoe up, one shoe down. This simple act of getting to my room seems insurmountable; I haven't walked more than two thousand steps a day in two years. This actually feels like a gross *mis*step, with my too- large luggage, my handicapped body and thousands of miles from home. How did I think I could manage this trip in a tiny medieval town perched on the limestone cliffs of Vaison-la-Romaine in Provence, France? I look up the incline and close my eyes. In my condition I need a key card, room service and bellhop.

I glance around the stairwell to make sure no one is watching my pathetic arrival and begin to climb, the weight of the hard-cased bag becoming heavier by the minute. Half-crawling, mostly clinging I finally pull myself up the forty-two steps to room No. 2. Gasping, holding my roller bag at bay with my foot, the key does not fit into the keyhole. I wiggle, turn, reinsert the unwieldy brass baton over and over, dropping it several times in the process. Finally — twice to the right, three clicks, grab the handle, push — works. A smell not unlike wet dog springs at me as I shoulder open the door and kick-roll my regrettable suitcase across the tiles. Inside, the shiny aqua satin bedspread, heavily curtained window, deep cavern of darkness makes me want to run back to the train station. I chastise myself aloud *buck up* and wipe the sweat off my upper lip. Dropping my purse on the desk, I adjust the chair to face the window and pull out my pain medications.

A desk, I think, ironic when I haven't written more than a page in two years.

After dinner that night — petite hors d'oeuvre, vin Rosé, tomato confit spooned onto slices of chewy bread, fork-tender pork, more than I have eaten in a week — I open the rusty window latch, push wide the six-foot-high panes and blossoms of a wild, white rose spill over the three-foot-deep sill. The scent is incomparable. I am heavy with fatigue in a pleasurable way and can't wait for bed.

Unbelievably, my stomach feels fine; I have not run to the toilet in distress for hours. My resected colon, which had been rejecting anything vaguely vegetable for twenty-four months, did not flinch at duck paté. I set out my clothes for tomorrow's workshop then slide between the sheets, leaving the window open. The air shimmers with bees. Still light at ten o'clock, the rose moon rises anyways. The cobblestone street below is absolutely silent: as sleep takes me I assure myself *you can always sit out the tour*. I dream of birdsong.

The busy schedule of walking, eating, writing, consuming banquettes gives me no time to think about my body: I tour Roman ruins, swirl and spit on wine tours, haggle at the open-air market. I lace up my sneakers each morning and am the first one at breakfast. On day three I have written a paragraph, walked ten thousand steps and taken several long, hot baths without thinking anything but *what's next*. I inquire and find out the serenade lulling me to sleep each night is the mating call of the elusive European Nightingale. I have not opened my pills.

Mid-way through the week I hungrily lick creme brûlée from the back of my spoon, as silky as sex on a summer afternoon. I hadn't been feeling an ounce of attractive over the last two years but suddenly my body feels worthy. Just then, like a capricious, invisible nymph the mistral wind slams across the table, tosses my napkin towards the sky and hurtles a bread basket over the wall. Green lettuces set sail. My *saumon avec l'huile d'olive* shivers. I part my lips to sip more wine and end up with a hank of hair in my mouth. I laugh and laugh and laugh and sweep the crumbs from my lap.

On the last day there is a group walking trip, the destination an ancient village far off on the next hillside, over four kilometers each way. The leader gives me walking sticks; the sound of the tips hitting the gravel is rhythmic. Along the road poppies are blooming on the hillsides, birds are louder than our conversation. The road turns to dirt path surrounded by terraced grape vines, fields of blue flax, wild sweet peas, livid yellow scotch broom, deep-green pin oak.

I get there. I rest. I lean back against the side of an icy stone church and eat almond macaroons. Peace settles in my bones.

We meander back in the receding day: I have 24,000 steps on my pedometer.

I found wellness in that room full of roses in the ancient hills of Provence; a place that reminded my body and myself that healing is not found in a bottle but can be as simple as opening a window while the moon slips over tiled rooftops and listening to the night bird sing.

Lauren Burstein
Song
Poetry

When the devil's played your fate,
When your mind's a mere worn weight,
Music helps you navigate,
And not just that of strings, horns, and keys,
But the kind that sets you free,
From all the worry and the pain,
The voices so ingrained,
In who we are and what we've become,
We forget there's a constant hum,
Of sound so sweet and bold,
The dreams we once foretold,
Belie the cruel, new, ugly rhyme,
And in it we can surely find,
A key to turn our ways around,
And become one with love and sound.

Photograph by D Ferrara

Sophie Stach Virgilio
Broken
NonFiction

He was different.

He was different and it wasn't because he was in a wheelchair. It was everything else about him that made him unusual. He was wearing several shirts and two jackets even though it was a warm outside. Plastic bags hung from each arm of his chair. Clothing was sticking out of some of these bags. Canned goods poked out of the others. Especially noticeable was the large blue sweat shirt that covered his head and face. Written on the front of the shirt, in large white letters was the word BROKEN.

I usually saw this man only in the morning as he rode on the Asbury boardwalk. He was always dressed the same; his head and face were always covered with that same blue shirt. It seemed that he intentionally made himself inaccessible, unreachable and disconnected from everything and everyone. It was obvious that he wanted to be left alone.

I saw so much fear, desperation and sadness beneath this separation. I never heard the sound of his voice because he never spoke to anybody. I did say, "Good morning," several times but he never answered. The few brown strands of his beard that were visible despite the cover told me that he was young. That's all I knew about him. It wasn't much.

One morning, I was surprised to see him inside the Asbury Park Arcade by the coffee shop that was crowded with people. He was sitting in his wheelchair and a young woman was standing behind him. She was laughing, talking and making hand gestures above his head as he sat there silently unmoved. Five feet in front this bizarre scene was a man who was taking their picture. Both the photographer and his female friend looked pampered to perfection, a sharp contrast to the invisible soul with the cover over his head. I was shocked and disgusted

They were treating this silent, gentle man as an amusement, a joke, a freak! I wondered who was broken.

Charlotte Crowder
Fear
Fiction

Fran was not a woman with many fears. She had absorbed life's blows and grown strong, capable. She walked city streets with a confident stride. She forgot to lock the door when her husband was away. She did not obsess about fatal diseases or freak accidents. She had worked to overcome her one irrational fear, becoming a good swimmer with a strong stroke. She held her head above the surface, in complete control unless a chance wave dunked her. Then panic welled. She imagined the depths below infested with blood-sucking creatures, waterweeds entangling her, pulling her down where she would never breathe again. She came sputtering to the surface, gasping for air like a strangulation victim, heart thundering.

Through some freak of genetics, Fran passed on this fear of the water. Four-year-old Liz, otherwise outgoing, sat cringing at the poolside, her body packed into iridescent Lycra. Each buoyed by a yellow foam bubble, her classmates paddled around the instructor, a young man with swim racer's shoulder muscles. To coax her, he splashed Liz's toes with water. She pulled them away as from an electrical current and buried her chin against her chest. Her mouth was taut, as if set against intense physical pain. The instructor was cowed by her stubborn refusal. He grinned sheepishly, awkward with his too-big shoulders, defeated by a tiny girl.

Fran sat on the bench with the mothers, each oblivious of the others as she doted on her own child. They wore sweat suits, the oversized shirts a testament to the sexlessness of early motherhood. All were barefooted. Fran's long feet splayed, her high arch just clearing a rivulet of water streaming across the turquoise tiles.

With the flourish of a performing magician, the instructor tipped the contents of a bucket into the pool, scattering rubber ducks. The children, all but Liz, shrieked with delight. Kicking up a chlorine-scented froth, they pumped through the water toward the ducks. Liz sat on the side of the pool and clung to the rail.

"Put your toes in, Liz," Fran urged. The little girl shook her head wildly, and Fran glanced at the other mothers along the bench, who momentarily suppressed the glow of maternal pride to throw her sympathetic looks. Fran shrugged and withdrew to let them gloat over their children's accomplishments, the bubbles they blew, the rhythm of their dog paddles.

In the dense air of the locker room, the mothers chased after the naked tots with terry towels, caught them up in their arms, and rubbed them dry as they wriggled. Screams and giggles echoed off the tile walls. Freed from her ordeal, Liz was chipper. She chatted to Fran as she struggled to pull up her overalls.

In the car, they played a guessing game. "You first," Liz urged as Fran pulled out of the YMCA parking lot onto the main street.

"I'm thinking of an animal with a long neck," Fran said, "with spots that eats leaves."

"A snake."

"No, not a snake. It has legs."

As Fran approached the intersection, an eighteen-wheeler inched off the exit ramp from the interstate. The light was green, but Fran slowed and stopped to allow the truck, which dwarfed her car, to turn onto the crossroad in front of her. The truck straddled both lanes, cab and trailer at odd angles like a giant broken slinky. Behind Fran's car, a horn blared.

"A bunny," Liz guessed.

The tractor trailer moved through the intersection in slow motion and the driver behind Fran continued to honk his horn.

"No, it eats leaves, but it's much bigger than a bunny."

When the intersection was clear, the light turned yellow. Fran remained at a stop. She would wait this light out. The driver behind her sat on his horn. Fran looked back through her rearview mirror. Irate, the man waved his arms about in fury.

"Aw, cool it, buddy," Fran waved her arms, mocking him.

The light turned red. Again, the driver blasted his horn. In the rearview mirror Fran saw his eyes narrow in anger. She gave him the finger, holding it up to the mirror, and watched the color rise up his neck and over his face. In a second, he was out of his car, storming toward Fran's, his legs pumping. Fran shot a glace back over her shoulder, checked the door was locked. Liz's eyes, big in her small face, reflected Fran's fear back at her. The light was still red. Fran sat up straight as the man approached her side window. He was slight, shorter than Fran, young, though his hairline was receding. He wore an overcoat and a business suit. Fran looked up at his face, now drained of all color. He was screaming. "If you flip me the bird, you better be ready to get out here and throw a few punches."

Fran sat motionless, her face muscles set. The words were ridiculous, but the threat was real. The man held his balled fist in front of her face on the other side of the glass. She stared, her mouth open in disbelief, as he pulled his arm back and struck the window with force that shook the car. She waited for the crash of glass, pain, blood, Liz's wails, ambulance sirens, but the window did not break. Their eyes still met, his small and mean, hers wide and questioning. He turned and stomped back to his car, impotent in his fury. The light turned green and Fran pulled slowly through the intersection to the side of the road, where she sat for several minutes breathing deeply. Liz was silent.

When she began to drive again, the tears came, streaming hot down her face, still taut with shock. She drove for more than a mile and then reached back to Liz in her car seat. Liz reached her little hand forward and squeezed Fran's hard.

"Is it a horse?" Liz asked.

"What?" Fran asked, then laughed through her tears, "No, it's a giraffe."

Jen OConnor
The Stone Woman (2005 – 2014)
NonFiction and Photography

      She kneels on a pedestal beside the blue Mediterranean – a stone woman – a piece of public art – improbable in this small town on the coast of Sicily. It is 2005 and I am here because this is where my grandparent came from, Terrasini, twenty miles west of Palermo.
In profile, the left half of her body visible, balancing between her knees

Stone Woman 2005 Photograph by Jen OConnor

an enormous flat striated disk - a seashell. Her cheek rests on the top of the shell; her eyes closed. Her hair is slicked back against her head as if wet from the sea.

Her long unadorned dress clings tightly to her body, revealing the prominent curves of breast and hip. Yet she looks to be majestically tall and slender, the sculpting style reminiscent of Art Deco of the 1920s or 30s. The definition of the sculpting is so subtle, the light grey stone weathered and sprinkled overall with verdigris, that the woman and her shell seem inseparable.

The plaque on her pedestal is too worn to read, but that doesn't matter. She is just for me – a magical sea nymph sprung from the sea and the rocks, cradling her precious shell.

I take only one picture and later, when I'm home, I enlarge, frame and hang it in my living room where it still is today.
In 2010 I returned to Terrasini and sought out the stone sculpture. It was covered with black graffiti. Even the back, which I had not looked at before, had been horribly defaced. I took a few pictures but I knew the magic was gone. The sea nymph lived now only in the picture in my living room.

In a writing workshop in 2014 I am asked to write about a piece of art that has great meaning for me. I know I will write about the sea nymph as I first saw her. I look long and hard at the picture in my living room and, although I don't want to, I find myself looking at the photos from 2010. And when I do, I realize that time and my own history have freed me to develop a new interpretation nine years later.

I research flat disc seashells and learn this one is a Sunray Venus. My thoughts fly to Botticelli's Birth of Venus, his vision of the goddess emerging from an enormous seashell. And now that I am looking at pictures of the stone woman from all angles I see that she is Venus too, but the shell is emerging from her, from the center of her body. She is balancing it between her legs, resting it between her breasts and cradling it against her cheek. To me, it is her own womb.

I see all this now because in 2005 I had not yet come out as a Lesbian to myself – or anyone else. In 2010 when I saw the statue the second time, I was out to myself but still too much of a coward to reveal my nature to others.

Finally, in 2011, I made the great leap. I declared myself a lover of women and opened my heart to all. There were many surprises – bad and good. Of the good, one was my re-awakening to the stone woman. Now I imagine her as a self-sufficient goddess who has loved and caressed only other women and that kind of courage has transformed her into this miraculous creature of woman and womb, capable of anything.

I look more closely at the photos from 2010. Most of the graffiti is on the shell—her womb. Much of the writing is illegible, but it is clear that they are all names: Giuseppe, Rosa, Pietro, Josetta, Mari Rosi.

The portrait of the original, unmarked Stone Woman still rests in my living room. I look at it often, knowing now that she has birthed many children. And I am one of them.

Stone Woman 2010 Photograph by Jen OConnor

Jen OConnor
A Back To School Litany
Poetry

Beg some lunch money from my father
School starts tomorrow
Break the news to Fido and Fluffy
and the goldfish I forgot to name
Tell my mother I'll need a new uniform
I tried mine on today
and couldn't get it over my chest
School starts tomorrow
Say good-bye to Dolores
cause she goes to St. Englebert's in the city
Tomorrow
Realize there's no way to avoid algebra
unless I die in my sleep tonight
School starts tomorrow
Steal my sister's lip gloss and eyeliner
and blame it on Aunt Mimi 'cause
she steals stuff at Macy's all the time anyway
Pray that Mr. Granger got hit by a bus
so I won't have to go into the cloakroom with him again

School starts tomorrow
Take one last run down the street to Maisie's Ice Cream
and get two scoops of chocolate with sprinkles and M&M's in a
waffle cone that Lenny will give me for free
Work up the nerve to tell Miss Borelli after English class
that I love Dolores the way Jason and Margaret in
eleventh grade love each other and I want to go off to St.
Englebert's with her

Tomorrow
Tell Miss Borelli what Mr. Granger does to me
Or maybe not
School starts tomorrow.

Walking on Air Photograph by Ria Moolgie

Sabrina Ito
Goddess Rituals
Poetry

We press our freshly manicured toes,
glossy, immaculate, impossibly pink,
into the cool, tight-packed expanse
of freshly-left, white powder sand
that sighs with relief each time
it flattens under the tide breaks.
We are moon-lit, as the waves,
rolling, silky and flowing,
in our Fair Trade layers
of hemp-woven scarves.
We are all undulating skirt hems,
chaffing, bra-less nipples,
bony bangled arms, from which swing
loose-skinned elbows
and ripped, recyclable bags,
now bursting with wedding rings,
love letters, yellowing, moth-eaten veils.
Our plans? At the stroke of midnight, we light everything on fire.
Because meditation and yoga

are no longer helping.
Because vision-boards and self-help books
are a waste of time.
Because Tinder and Match
only yield disappointment.
Because *Macbeth*'s Three Witches
no longer terrify, but inspire.

Let us no longer quell, but ignite fervent fires—
as did Pele, as did Vesta, as did Jowangsin,
let us incinerate past trappings before letting new love in.
We'll release loss and divorce to the smoke and the stars,
faces shining from hot licks of flame,
smiles blotted thick
with red lipstick.

Photograph by Jeff Talarigo

Susan Eve Haar
My Brother: What I Know So Far
NonFiction

When I was six, he was ten. We moved to London.

I got the good bedroom, but I gave it to him.

There was no central heating. We cut apples into crinkled halves and cooked them in the coals. We had a Dutch babysitter named Ali BaBa. She was blonde. She dropped a kitchen knife; it stuck into her foot. There was a mulberry tree with purple berries that stained. There was an Aga stove in the kitchen. I had a gray school uniform with a pleated skirt. I had a beret and a square pin etched with a yellow tree. A white shirt and a little tie.

He had nightmares about the fox and the witch. He got in fights. He came home with blood and mud and grass stuck up his nose. He got caned at school.

I caught up, I learned to read and write cursive and walk in line. I had piano lessons and read Grimm's fairy tales and *The Jungle Book*. My friend Evon's mother served fried cat food. My friend Judy's father had a chauffeur. We walked on the stone walls around the house single file. It was very high. The chestnuts were shaped like maces, we stomped on them; the nut popped out sometimes. I carved tiny chestnut baskets. A bead fit inside. They dried out and cracked.

There was a camel saddle in the living room. He began to pull out his eyelashes. He pulled out all his eyelashes and put Vaseline on the edges. His eyelids were pink and very thick, he was a blue-eyed lizard. Sometimes the neighbor boy threw stones and dinky toys over the wall. He kept the toys. He collected things. He had arrowheads and a replica Egyptian cat with a black collar and a Steiff tiger with jointed legs.

At night the house sucked my breath away. I lay patient as a little toad under a stone, waiting for the air to come back. I was quiet except for the noises. Sometimes I steamed with a towel over my head. My face got too hot, and stuff dripped into the boiling water and curdled. Sometimes he locked us in the bathroom. I sat on the edge of the slipper tub; it was cold. He cut the bottoms of his feet with a razor blade. He made a crisscross pattern on the soles, there was not much blood on account of the callouses. More blood on the pads under his toes. I would never tell.

I wanted to be teacher's pet. She called me to the front of the room and pinned back my hair with bobby pins. I was dirty. There was bubblegum in my hair. It was long. Stuff stuck to it. My mother cut my bangs straight across sometimes. I brought Droste's chocolate to school so I could make friends.

We went back to Cambridge. His room had orange walls. There were shelves around the room, he had collections. He collected stilettos and flick knives and bayonets and spears and coins. He traded stamps, mounting them in albums with hinges, each page covered with a sheet of translucent paper. My hamster had babies. The father ate the leg off one. It could still climb. He called it Stumpy. He had a newt called Knute Rockne, it crawled out of the aquarium and dried up on the heat register. Sometimes he hurt me. I believed if I fought like a berserker, in a trance-like fury, I would survive.

We traveled. We wore red sweaters and learned to count to ten in many languages. There was always the children's table. In France we drank wine. I got drunk and jumped on the beds in strangers' hotel rooms. He ate only veal cutlets and peanut butter. I ate kidneys and Petit-suisse. I cut my fingers with his jackknife and ran cold water over my hand. My mother did not stop reading, the book had a red cover. Pressure, she said. I picked holes in my arms and read a lot of Russian science fiction.

There was screaming. I threw up. His hair fell out. He wore a terrible toupee. He was seventeen.

He left.

***

The woman he brought to stay said she has a plate in the top of her head; she was a *Playboy* centerfold and a paramour of Richard Dreyfuss. Her parents were neurosurgeons. Her children were geniuses. She was going to die soon. She needed a lot of diamonds. She had extensions and plastic nails. She spent two hours in my bathroom. He waited like a dog. I tried to buy the baby, but she left it someplace in Houston.

***

He had a cat named Moniffa.

***

When he threw the baby up in the air, the baby stopped crying.

And now he lives in a gated community in Las Vegas. He has five cats. The cats have bird movies and a courtyard. The cats are called "the people." The people tell him what to do; it is kind of a joke. His house stinks, the cats shit on the beds and rip up the furniture. I can't breathe. His black cat Puma, the one who'd had its head run over, walks with me like a dog.

There's a skull by the door with a light inside. He has a jar of belly fat from a woman's tummy tuck in Thailand. He has a collection of dried bats. He has devil figures with spiked tails from Día de los Muertos. He has masks of tigers and ghouls with fangs and glass eyeballs painted with thin, red veins. He has exploding shit. He has guns. He has gallon jars of pills. He has netsuke from the dead and gone, a clamshell with a fisherman inside holding an ivory pole and an ivory fish on the line, a crosshatched ivory turtle.

He buys a grave on Craigslist. He buys a casket. It's a bargain. He uses it for my mother. Then he gets another.

He dreams. My mother shoves open the doors of heaven and finds him worthy. He thinks about moving to Oakland. He has a lot of old Mercedes with rusted-out bodies. He has a giant, inflatable menorah he puts on his apartment building across from the mosque. He has a collection of Kitty Cat Klocks with tails that wag the hour. He has various children by various women.

***

I haven't seen his daughter in seventeen years. Her photos online are lurid, tangy with sex. But here she is. She stands, tentative, in the kitchen. She wears a light blue wool jacket with square shoulders. It covers her body to the knees. Her eyelashes are long like his. She is very tall. Her hair is crinkled blonde, pulled back tight in a knot. She has my aunt's green eyes, she has my father's lips, and her skin is dusky caramel. There is goat cheese and carrots and wine. She drinks. She is shy. She smiles like a cat. When she leaves, she hugs me.

I didn't know that she heard voices. The tormenters. I didn't know that she had weapons—pepper spray and tasers and a crowbar and a baseball bat. I didn't know she was afraid.

They have to get makeup.

They have to fight the landlord.

They have to look at apartments.

They have to go to the Apple store to get the voices out of her computer.

They cannot wait for the psychiatrist at Kaiser.

***

When she calls the police, he follows in his car.

This is what I know so far.

Jean Colonomos
How the Light Got In
Poetry

The ancient Greeks believed in destiny. When Oedipus was born, the seer,
Tiresias, predicted the infant would kill his father and marry his mother.
The child was taken to the mountains and left to die. A shepherd took pity
on the baby and Oedipus lived to fulfill the prophecy. Martha Graham's
"Night Journey" is based on this myth.

1
Dancers
like glints of steel,

        wing-footed messengers

A female Greek chorus

        twelve racing feet

        six cupped hands

    inscribed on our taut, flat palms
Jocasta and Oedipus' doom.

When a curtain descends,
after-image is what's left—

the whole cloth of Graham's ill-fated love life

with a much younger partner

the beauty of our sculpted bodies

leaving me in tears.

2
Those *buffalo jumps*
as we called them—

arms bent at the elbows,

leaping four times from a crouch

then

high jumps with our front and back legs

bent

the image of hovering monsters.

I danced out of myself with such ferocity
I wondered what inner fire
I was trying to put out,

Graham's extreme choreography
sending me to a place beyond language,

my body filled with astonishment's pleasure when

the force of six female dancers embodied one.

Jean Colonomos
Dear Marcia
Poetry

We were a matched pair; the blood said so when we sliced our thumbs in the dressing room. At fourteen I couldn't compete with your ripening body. Mine was a plank. Yet we twinned in ballerina talent, you with your perfect ballet-body alignment and strong feet arched like hooks, and me with my thirty-two fouettés or whip turns where each landing before the next was an exclamation point. It was as if some force were driving me out of myself to leave all boundaries behind. What we hid from our parents was the plan to quit school at sixteen to join the Metropolitan Opera Ballet. When we doubted ourselves, we were sure we'd be asked to join this progressive company when in 1951, Janet Collins became the first African-American to be a full-time soloist in ballet's white world: dear Janet Collins, a slip of a woman we'd sometimes watch rehearse before afternoon class absorbing how she moved. The ease with which she executed the most complicated choreography was a language our bodies longed to speak. M and I were going to live together in the great city of New York and that plot kept us going through a gloomy and spotted adolescence. Oh Marcia, everywhere we turned, we stretched towards the invisible light. This was the love we shared. A dancer's life—

millions of spinning miles clocked
on her odometer.

Painting by Holly Tappen

Jean Colonomos
The Temple Of The Pelvic Truth
Poetry

for the Martha Graham dance students, circa 1960s

       We are the Graham crackers
       who worship at the Temple of the Pelvic Truth.
       We pray to the Kundalini and Duende Goddesses
       where our contractions and releases,
       like these holy preachings, begin
       at the base of our spines. We start
       our rituals on the floor, some of us
       anticipating the class's tone from
       the pianist accompanying that day.
       Tom, our least favorite,
       bangs out a 4/4 beat, missing
       the sensuous innuendos
       in Martha's movement vocabulary.
       A small group like me enjoys drip-dry jazz king Ralph.
       He teases out a note
       and then   silence.
       When we're about to give up, he plunks
       another note to inform our next move.

And then there's Stanley
whose Chopinesque chords
seep into our bodies. When he plays,
we forget how imperfect we are,
how shaky is our balance, our contractions
as our beings sing with ecstasy's song.

Brandon French
Pop Goes the Weasel
Fiction

"Daddy's having an affair," Gertrude Kirschenbaum shouted into her cell phone as soon as she got home from The Jewish Federation, where she worked as a fundraiser. "Get over here."

"What?" her brother Ansel said, but Gertrude had already hung up.

She stormed through the townhouse in search of her father's admission paperwork to the Compassionate Hebrew Home. Passing through the kitchen, she cursed Jimenez the gardener, who had once again forgotten to trim the bougainvillea that had burgeoned riotously over the summer and was now blocking the sunlight from the greenhouse window, yelled at her teenage son Trevor, who she suspected was jerking off in the locked hallway bathroom, and snapped at Seymour the Newfoundland, whose slumbering immensity was obstructing the entrance to the den that served as an office.

Why me? she asked whatever God or ghost was lurking behind the pale blue walls or listening through the optic white ceiling. *Why is this my problem?* Why the hell had the Administrator of the Hebrew Home called *her* about her father instead of calling her brother, the lawyer, or her father's brother Harry, who still had most of his marbles, or her mother, who was his *wife*, for God's sake?

Neither God nor ghost replied.

The next afternoon, Gertrude and Ansel sat in front of the Hebrew Home Administrator, Elaine Markowitz, and the Home's visiting psychologist, Dr. Edie Bloom. Gertrude's left arm became stuck in her blazer as she struggled to remove it before she had a hot flash. Her brother looked at her helplessly, as if a tyrannosaurus had her halfway swallowed and there was no way to rescue her from its jaws.

"Grab the sleeve," she hissed, already incensed at what she anticipated would be another burden for her to shoulder. Ansel reached over apprehensively, fearing his sister might smite him if he failed to disengage her arm.

"Thank you both for coming," Elaine Markowitz began.

"Did we have a choice?" Gertrude mumbled, folding her blazer carefully before placing it in her carryall.

Elaine Markowitz smiled stiffly, having dealt with many menopausal adult children of aging parents in her eleven-year reign as Administrator.

"We have a challenge," she began, the word *problem* permanently excised from the Hebrew Home's lexicon. "Jacob has formed a romantic alliance with another resident."

"Are you sure?" Ansel said, still struggling to comprehend that his decrepit, senile father was having an affair.

"I told you, pop's in love with another woman," Gertrude said, loud enough for anyone passing in the hallway to hear.

"Well, not exactly," Dr. Edie Bloom interjected. "The object of Jacob's affection is a gentleman named Herbert."

"Dad's not gay," Ansel said, glancing quickly at his sister for validation.

"Oh my Gawd," Gertrude wailed, as if she'd just been given a cancer diagnosis.

"Their public displays have been upsetting the families of other residents," Elaine Markowitz said. "I'm afraid we may have to ask you to place your father somewhere else if he doesn't stop."

"What about the *other* guy?" Gertrude demanded.

"Herbert was here first," Dr. Edie Bloom said.

"But what if *he* started it?" Gertrude persisted.

"It doesn't matter," Elaine Markowitz said.

As soon as the meeting ended, Gertrude went to the doorway of the Hebrew Home's lounge, looking around at the residents, who had already finished their dinner by 4:30. The whole place had a smell she couldn't identify—not bleachy like cleaning solution, or yummy like banana bread, or pungent like boiled cabbage or fried fish. It must have been old people's smell, she thought, that sickly sweet odor of lost muscle mass and sagging, spotted flesh.

"Which one is Herbert?" she asked a woman playing canasta.

"Who?"

"Herbert."

"Who?" another woman asked the first one.

"Herbert," the first woman said.

"Who?" the third canasta player asked, looking up from her cards.

Was everyone here hard of hearing, Gertrude wondered. The place sounded like an owl sanctuary.

All three canasta players twisted around in their seats to look for Herbert.

"Over there," one of the women said, pointing to a dapper little man sitting by himself at a small round table, working on a crossword puzzle.

Gertrude went over to him and sat down in an empty chair.

"I hear you and my father are friends."

"I beg your pardon?"

Gertrude repeated herself, louder.

"I'm not hard of hearing," Herbert said with a pleasant smile. "I just don't know who you're referring to."

"Jacob Steinmetz."

"Ah, yes, Jacob. A lovely man, despite the —." He stopped short of the word *dementia*. "You look a little like him."

"My father's married, you know."

"That so?"

"To my mother."

"Uh-huh," Herbert said, his eyebrows raised questioningly.

"He's not gay," Gertrude said.

"I see," Herbert said, fidgeting with his pencil point as if it needed sharpening.

"He's not a fairy," she said, in case he did not know the current terminology.

"All right," he said, nodding, and opened his palms in anticipation of her point. "So?"

"So you should leave him alone."

The old gentleman looked dismayed. "Have I done something to —?"

"Mrs. Markowitz said you two are playing hide-the-salami."

"The what?"

"Having sex. And since my father isn't homosexual, I'm assuming *you're* the —." She wondered if there was a less inflammatory word than *perpetrator*.

"I think the person you're looking for is Herbert Schlosser. I'm Herbert Marcus."

"Oh, I beg your pardon," Gertrude said, turning bright scarlet and scrambling to her feet. "I'm so sorry. Those women said—."

"That's alright," he said without rancor and returned to where he'd left off— https://www.snopes.com/fact-check/police-pop-hoods/ 18 across, seven letters, another word for folly.

Gertrude headed for the front door and burst into the moonlight as if she'd been launched. By the time she reached her Lexus, she was fighting back tears.

The following Saturday, Gertrude belted her father and Herbert Schlosser into the back seat of her car like two boys she was chauffeuring to Little League.

"Where do you want to go?" she asked.

"Pink," her father said.

"Pinks? You want hot dogs?"

"Yes," her father said, giggling at Herbert like a little girl.

"Hot dogs," Herbert agreed, his lips leaking a little saliva in anticipation. Then he made a grab for Jacob's cell phone, and a scuffle ensued.

"Behave yourselves," Gertrude shouted, glaring at them in the rearview mirror. What had become of her masterful father, the former owner of the largest Toyota dealership in Santa Monica, that shrewd, virile hero of her childhood? A terrifying specter of her own geriatric future vaulted across Gertrude's mind.

She had wanted to see how her father and Herbert interacted with each other outside the Home, still hoping that their relationship was innocent. *Okay, so they crawled into bed with each other like boy scouts camping out. Did that mean they were gay?* It suddenly occurred to her that maybe boy scouts *did* fool around with each other sexually when they camped out. Maybe that's what Trevor had done.

"Ugh," she said out loud, squirming in her seat. *Who needs to think such thoughts?*

That night, in bed with her husband Maury, Gertrude worried aloud about her father's attachment to Herbert.

"They're like a couple of six-year-olds," she said. "They squirted ketchup and mustard at each other at Pinks until I threatened to spank them. And on the way back to the Home, they wouldn't stop kissing each other."

"You took them to Pinks?" Maury asked at the tail end of a yawn.

"They wanted hot dogs," Gertrude said. "Do you think they're really messing around with each other?"

"You mean sex?"

"I guess."

"Isn't your dad kind of old for that?"

"I don't know. How old is too old?"

"Fifty-eight," Maury said, reaching out and embracing Gertrude, whose back was turned to him.

"What are you doing?" she said.

"Messing around. All that sex talk —"

Gertrude turned over to face him. It was the first time he'd initiated anything in months.

"So the idea of two old men screwing each other is turning you on?" she asked.

"Keep that up and it'll go away."

Gertrude's hands moved toward her husband beneath the covers, reaching for the familiar warmth of his skin. "I don't want it to go away," she said, kissing him happily on the mouth.

A few days later, Gertrude invited her mother to lunch at Joan's on Third, one of Essie's favorite restaurants. Gertrude ordered the three-salad combo. Essie opted for the Chinese chicken salad. They found a small table at the back of the restaurant, where it was less crowded and noisy.

"So, mom," Gertrude began. "How are you holding up?"

"You probably think I'm upset about daddy, but I'm not."

"Who told you?"

"Your brother."

"That little shit. He promised he wouldn't."

"Your father was insatiable, Gerty," Essie said, something Gertrude would gladly have spent the rest of her life not knowing. "And don't think this is the first time he's been unfaithful. I say, let some other woman deal with him. Good riddance."

"It's not a woman."

"Oh, really?" Essie looked surprised but then she began to laugh.

"Mom! It's not funny."

"Of course it is."

"You won't think so if they kick dad out and he has to come home and live with you again."

"Like hell he will," Essie said. She had been an advertising executive in a large agency before she retired and didn't tolerate anyone

228

pushing her around. "Gerty," she'd lectured her daughter as a teenager, "somebody punches you, you punch them right back. That's how you make them see who's who and what's what."

"There are eleven couples having affairs in the Hebrew Home," Gertrude announced to Elaine Markowitz, who looked especially tired that Friday after two health emergencies in the morning and Shabbat looming. "Ten of them are men and women," Gertrude went on, "so obviously your problem is with homosexuality and that's discrimination." She had spent Sunday gathering gossip about the residents, and Monday checking out the law.

"Look, Mrs. Kirschenbaum, we know there are romantic liaisons between some of the residents, including a few gay ones. They're usually fleeting, and we don't object unless their behavior gets out of hand. But sometimes the husbands and wives of the residents feel rejected and betrayed by their spouses and they want us to intervene."

"My mother doesn't give a damn about it," Gertrude said.

"Unfortunately, Herbert's wife *does*."

The next weekend, Herbert's wife brought their grandson to visit and the little boy kept playing *Pop Goes the Weasel* on his jack-in-the-box.

"*All around the mulberry bush, the monkey chased the weasel, the monkey fell down and oh, what a sound, pop goes the weasel.*"

After the twelfth repetition, Jacob popped along with the weasel, jumping onto the four-year-old and throttling him violently.

"He doesn't know how big he is," Gertrude argued later in her father's defense. "He thinks he's a little kid."

The next night, Gertrude and her brother moved their father out of the Hebrew Home and settled him temporarily in the Kirschenbaum's guest room. Herbert's wife had taken her husband out for dinner that evening so the two men wouldn't make a scene. Jacob didn't seem to understand what was happening.

In bed with Maury later, Gertrude began to cry.

"I feel so bad for him," she said. "First he lost his mind and now he's lost his friend. It's like the whole world has played a dirty trick on him."

Maury pulled her close and rocked her.

"Sometimes, honey, forgetting is a gift," he said. "Maybe tomorrow he won't remember today."

"My grandpa's a fag," Gertrude overheard her son say on his cellphone as he munched on a gargantuan chocolate chip cookie.

"He is not!" she shouted from the kitchen. "Who are you talking to?"

"Hang on a minute," Trevor whispered and quickly retreated to his room.

Gertrude finished putting the dinner dishes into the dishwasher and came into the living room, dropping down on the couch next to her father with an exhausted sigh. Jacob was watching, or at least staring at, *Mamma Mia*. At least he was sitting quietly, she thought, and not crying anymore.

On the weekdays, a nursing student was keeping an eye on Jacob while Gertrude and Maury were at work. Saturdays, Gertrude's mother took over the vigil although Jacob no longer recognized his wife of forty-seven years. On Sundays, Gertrude's brother and sister-in-law babysat Jacob while Gertrude and Maury played golf. But in the evenings, Gertrude was on duty, keeping her father company and helping him get ready for bed.

"Daddy," she said, smiling at him and gently patting his hand. He looked at her with hazy familiarity, as if he'd met her long ago but couldn't quite place her. Gertrude began to notice that the dead flower odor of the Hebrew Home was permeating the living room like a creeping fog.

It's temporary, Gertrude reassured everybody while they searched for another placement for Jacob, but it had already been a month of polite and not-so-polite refusals from most of the better venues and the family was running out of steam.

Jacob kept asking for Herbert although he could no longer remember Herbert's name. "Where is *he*?" he repeated, gazing tearfully at anyone within earshot. "Herbert is fine," they all answered, except for Trevor, who said, "Face it, grandpa. You fucked up."

Trevor got a kick out of humming "Pop Goes the Weasel," hoping to get a rise out of his grandfather. "By the way," he explained to the old man after googling the nursery rhyme, "it's not about an animal at all. The weasel's part of a spinning wheel that goes pop. Isn't that weird?" When Jacob didn't respond, Trevor shouted, "Pop, pop, pop, pop, pop!" until his grandfather clapped his hands over his ears and shrieked.

"Why are boys so cruel?" Gertrude asked her husband as they were out walking Seymour that evening.

Maury shrugged. "Girls can be cruel, too. You know, 'mean girls.'"

"It's not the same," Gertrude said.

She loved her son, of course, but at times she wished he'd been a daughter, someone who ran on estrogen rather than testosterone so they could commiserate.

"Wait 'til *you* get old," she chided her son after putting his grandfather to bed. Trevor, who'd been stretched out on his bed playing Candy Crush, looked up at his mother as if she had just offered him a lap dance.

"Are you crazy?" he said, his dark eyes wide with disbelief. Before Gertrude could tell him that nobody thought they were going to get old, especially when they were young, Trevor rolled over, emitted a dismissive little fart and returned his attention to the game.

Half Staff by Brigitte Carroll

John E. Simonds
Be Careful, Very Careful
Poetry

"The highest risk is for elderly population with underlying health
conditions. The elderly population must be very, very careful.
In particular, we are strongly advising that nursing homes for the elderly
suspend all medically unnecessary visits. In general, older Americans
should also avoid nonessential travel in crowded areas." President Donald
Trump, White House speech to nation. March 11, 2020.

This is the way the world could end,
not with a bang but a quarantine.
First the border portcullis,
then the rest-home barbed wire,
as the herd drive to cure
corrals the virus in elders.
Contain the old as tantamount victims,
the White House says, channeling flash
of Molokai's leprosy enclaves.
Seniors may carry the spreading crown,
so keep to yourself, says the oldster-in-chief,

quietly aging on screen with his peach-toned corona,
away from the nodding wisdom of his hollow men.
Serpent heads on the winding caduceus
speak with two voices at once:
disconnect and don't panic;
wash your hands and worry,
but stay calm and keep distance.
Planes aren't flying, but stay grounded in faith.
Borders are closing, but reach out to help.
Cleanliness is next to godliness,
but thy rod and staff seem little comfort here.
Did dinosaurs stand taller
against glaciers and asteroids,
or were they advised to dress warmer
but keep their blood cool;
avoid crowds and swamps,
and those falling gray spaceballs
with tufty red burstings?
We have nothing to fear but ourselves,
our answers and what we share
with others before sealing our lips and shores,
gating our yards and locking our doors.
We're closing down the grand vision of 2020,
one eye in the rearview to ensure
we've covered our "buts."
Be worried, but don't lose faith.
Be cautious, but don't lose nerve.
Collaborate, but don't congregate.
Lots of places for testing, but who has the kits?
Make smart choices, but do as you're told.
Civilization is on course to cancel,
easing the way with words like postpone.
Stay home and let us pay you
to leave each other alone.

Learning to live like cells under glass,
we're ever splitting, growing apart,
waiting for deficit deaths to decline
and a closing bell that grants
some of us chance to survive.

Barn Cats Photograph by D Ferrara

Jon Epstein
Shantytown Contraband
Fiction

"Okay, Jon-Bird," Steve says. He hands me a bulk of pesos equivalent to ten US dollars. "Knock twice on the door," he says, "pause, and knock twice again."

As dingy as our room is, at least it's safe and cozy. I don't mind the peeling wallpaper, or the streaked, long-since-washed windows, or the tattered curtains, or the dripping bathroom faucet. It's a fortress against the unstable, crime-ridden, impoverished comings and goings waiting outside the hotel front door.

"Here's the map, Jon-Bird." Danny hands me a piece of scrap paper with a diagram scratched out in pencil.

"Just stay on Carrera Diez," Steve says. "Go right on the first narrow dirt alley after the Tequendama.

"I wrote it all down, Steve," Danny says.

"White boys walking the streets of Bogotá is hazardous," Steve said yesterday afternoon when I lied about wanting to go to the corner bodega for some stationery, when I really wanted to sneak a forbidden international phone call to Lori back home.

"Are you sure this is a good idea?" I ask. The fact that Jesus's adobe hovel is within spitting distance of one of the many neighborhood police stations raises my hackles. I've scored pot a thousand times back in Hollywood, but Bogotá isn't Tinseltown, and I'm scared shitless.

"Stay alert," Steve says. "You can do this. Just don't make eye contact with anyone on the street."

"What do you mean?"

"Gee, Jon-Bird," Danny clucks in, "while traipsing around the streets of Bogotá," he uses his TV travel show host's voice, "one will likely witness some garden variety form of crime." Danny makes a sweeping gesture with his hands. "Muggings, back-alley knifings, and fatal or non-fatal vehicular hit-and-runs are a daily norm in the Emerald City."

"Just keep your head down and nose straight," Steve reassures. "I'm up for the Pepsi Challenge."

"Uh-huh." I'm not cut out for this deployment. "You guys are sure about this?"

"Sooner or later you're going to have to cut your teeth and log some solo street time," Steve says.

"Yeah, Jon-Bird," Danny says. "Other than the fact you have gringo blue eyes and pale skin," he jokes, "you'll be fine."

"All right," I reply, "if you guys say so." I open the door and walk out. I guess my mission is simple enough: walk a mile or so, score some sticky Colombian buds, and walk back to the hotel. Steve assured me Jesus is reliable, and after all, it's daytime and I will be walking a major boulevard.

I step out the open glass doors of Hotel Gerber. A man is cleaning the front window with some crumpled newspaper and a bucket of soapy water. *Systemas Americanos* is stenciled in black italic print on the opposite door.

It's springtime in the Latin American cocaine mecca. Cotton-candy clouds punctuate the high-altitude blue sky, while brownish smog hangs low in between the high-rise downtown buildings. The busy street is clogged with chugging buses, diesel trucks, and American cars from the 50s, mostly turned into taxis. Heavy foot traffic on both sides of the street makes it easy for me to become another anonymous face in the downtown crowd.

I pass a piñata store, a Western Union office, and a couple of haberdasheries, and then stop in front of the open double doors of a bustling *panadería*. The sweet, thick waft of freshly baked *pan y pastelirías i*s enticing. A large, aproned woman wearing a hairnet is decorating a wedding cake behind the plate-glass storefront window. I flash back to Martino's Bakery on Magnolia in Burbank, where I'd talked Mom and Dad into allowing me to order a large, moonscape-decorated cake for my seventh birthday. It was complete with a plastic toy astronaut and moon-buggy. I want to go inside for a fresh turnover and milk, but Steve's marching orders were explicit: "No stops in between," he mandated.

Before I head on my way to the weed connection, I take stock of my reflection in the window—green cords, short-sleeve plaid shirt, brown Top-Siders, and a green nylon windbreaker. I look conspicuous, but Steve told me, "dress like a student." And that's what I look like. *Is it over the top?* I imagine it's probably the right look to stay under the local law's radar, but not the best armor to ward off potential street toughs.

I continue down the boulevard. It feels about 65. The drifting clouds thicken, and the sunrays lessen.

I cross a small side street, and the next block changes dramatically. A legless man on a makeshift mechanic's creeper propels himself with his greasy, gloved hands directly at me. He stops at my feet and holds his right hand out. His clothes are tattered, and his dirty brown hair covers his dirty brown face.

I glance right and left and pull a 5 peso note from my pocket and extend it towards the man. He snatches it and shoves the bill in his pocket. Before I can blink, he makes haste in the opposite direction.

I continue down the row of boarded-up businesses and weed-ridden vacant lots. I pass by several open cardboard houses. Young, seemingly parentless kids eat from bowls with their hands, with faraway looks in their eyes.

I'm upon the Tequendama, Bogotá's high-rise, fancy-schmancy hotel. A uniformed doorman with gold-braided epaulets stands tall in his long coat and top hat, waiting to greet his next patron.

"Hola," I say. The man returns my greeting with a sneer. I try not to take it personally and pass the hotel. I spot the narrow dirt street and make a right off the heavily traveled avenue.

The narrow dirt path to Jesus's turns into timeworn cobblestone. There's a break in the clouds, and the muted sun hits the stones. They suddenly appear polished. The street steepens, climbing up the hillside to my destination.

I look at Danny's chicken-scratch map. I squint and think I make out the word dirt. Sure enough, the cobble turns to dry, hard-packed mud.

Straight ahead is a row of whitewashed adobe hovels with worn and faded green wooden doors that fit Steve's description. I glance back at my directions and see #7.

Across the back alley is a police station. Two officers are standing in front, smoking. I spot the door with a rusted iron numeral 7 hanging from a nail, surrounded by overgrown bougainvillea vines, an assortment of palms, and Colombian mahogany. The foliage has taken root in every square inch of unoccupied soil. Between the awesome vegetation and windowless shanties, I feel as though I've stepped into a *National Geographic*. I wonder about the shanty occupants. What they do and how they eke out a living.

I knock twice with a nervous staccato firmness. The off-center 7 pendulums. I pause and knock another two times.

The door cracks open. A woman's nose appears. I assume it's Jesus's wife.

"Hola," I say. "Yo soy amigo de Esteve Morgan." A hanging blanket blocks my view of their front room.

"Que necessitas?" she asks. *What do you need?*

"Yo aquí para la mota." *I am here for marijuana.*

"Entrar." She ushers me in quickly, so as not to draw any more attention from the police. I remember Steve told me her name was Esperanza.

"Gracias," I say.

"Siéntate." Esperanza offers me one of the two chairs they own. "Quieres café?"

"Por favor," I reply. I sit and sneak a peek here and there, not wanting to seem nosy. The place has a dirt floor, single-burner kerosene lamp, and white gas Coleman stove. The handmade Cachalú table and reed-bound chairs are the only furniture in the front room. They've divided the room by draping another wool blanket from a piece of clothesline, separating the kitchen and sitting area from the sleeping quarters.

"Esto ira bien con café." She brings me a homemade sweet roll and a cup of java.

"Gracias," I say. "Dondé esta Jesus?" I sip the strongest coffee I have ever ingested.

"El volverá pronto. El esta con nuestros hijos," she says. *He will return soon. He is with our kids.*

By the time I finish the brew, I feel as though I've put my finger in an electrical socket. The door opens, and I jump out of my skin.

"Hola." Jesus greets me with two small children. A young girl is holding Jesus's hand, and in the other dangles a woven wool doll. She looks up with her huge brown eyes, not sure what to make of the blue-eyed gringo, and then smiles generously, as toddlers do, innocent and unaware of their surroundings. The boy jumps into Esperanza's arms.

"Salir y jugar." He tells his kids to go outside and play.

I saw Jesus a couple of days ago when Steve bought some weed from him near the Mercado; Danny and I sat on one of the wooden benches scattered about the plaza and observed the clandestine buy go down.

"Hola," he says. "Me llamo Jesus. Mucho gusto."

"Hola, me llamo Juan," I say. "Equalmente." My high school Spanish allows me pleasantries before we get down to brass tacks.

"Cuántos quieres?" Jesus inquires. I take the rubber-banded bundle of pesos from my pants pocket.

"Estevo dijo que lo sabrías," I say—*Steve said you would know*—and hand Jesus the money. I've no clue what this will buy and don't need

241

to as Steve assured me Jesus is reliable.

Jesus leafs through the bills. "Un momento," he says and disappears behind the curtain. I hear the kids' playful laughter outside and admire the cleanliness of their digs.

Jesus emerges with a brown paper bag like Mom used to pack my lunches in.

"Aqui tenes; todas flores y muy fuerte," he says. *All buds*. I wonder what the wholesale cost of the weed is. Steve told me he always overpays to reward trustworthiness. No wonder Esperanza was so hospitable. "Tu jefe Esteve tiene un cortisone grande." Jesus praises Steve's generosity. "Dile que estoy gradecido." I suspect whatever the profit is, it'll probably feed his family for a week.

"Gracias." I take the bag of pot. "Puedo tener privacidad?" I ask if I can step behind their curtain room divider.

"Si," he says.

I do so and shove the bag into my pants. It's bulky and conspicuous; I untuck my shirt to hide the bulge. The volume is greater than I expected. I reenter the front room. "Muchas gracias," I say again. "Hasta la vista."

"Espere," Jesus says. He opens the door and pokes his head out and signals me to come. "Todo tranquilo."

I exit *la motarilla* and glance over my shoulder in the direction of the police station. Uniformed men are hanging out behind mosquito netting, talking, laughing, and smoking.

A lightning flash illuminates the sky. It's very close. In two winks explosive thunder rattles Jesus's flimsy corrugated tin roof. A cloudburst falls; instantly, I'm soaked, but don't mind. The rain will keep Johnny Law under dry cover.

I'm buzzed on caffeine and dart down the dirt path. Within moments, brown rivulets wash around my feet, as I hoof it back to the main drag.

The jammed traffic is moving like chocolate pudding gone mousse. There is much squeaking from the many vehicles operating with rubberless windshield wipers.

I pass the vacant lots and boarded-up buildings. The cardboard houses sag, and the children huddle together.

I duck into the dry doorway of a Bible store to readjust my package. A hanging store window sign says *cerrado*. Even though I'm Jewish, I'm haunted by the multitude of crosses, Jesus likenesses, and life-sized Mary's. Knowing but not knowing, I get a flash of what morality should look like, and my shoulders sink. I turn my back to the overdose of holiness and face the street.

Package better secured, I dash out onto the sidewalk. The rain's volume has increased, and the sky is solar-eclipsed dark; the cars with working headlights burn bright. The liquid locust canopy avails a safer passage back to the Gerber.

I expedite my pace, passing by a blur of wet stucco and squalor. Soon I'm running as fast as I can. I run, not knowing that's the story of my life and who I am. I am a runner. I run away. I run from myself. I run from those who love or once loved me. Ironically, I desire love, to be loved, and to love another, but can't, because I'm always running.

I race the remaining half-mile without looking over my shoulder.

I pass the *panadería* to the Gerber entrance. The plate-glass doors are now clean, albeit rain streaked. The rickety elevator is in use. I realize I'm dripping water and tracking whatever mud, muck, and miscellaneous street debris has clung to my shoes across the lobby carpet. The deskman doesn't look up from his paper, and I race up the five flights of stairs, two and three at a time. My heart is pumping, and my mind is fleetingly free. I rest my hand on my bulging shirt. I made it. I grabbed the brass ring. I went back and did it again, Jack. I've secured my first Morgan merit badge but have sacrificed so much. No sports. No dates. No yearbook. No prom. No cap. No gown. No graduation. I won't go to college. I won't satisfy my dad.

I continue to rush past the peeling wallpaper and threadbare carpet on my sprint up the last two flights of stairs. Running, always running, always as fast as I can.

Out of breath and soaking wet to the bone, I stand before our hotel room door. I knock out the secret tap. The door opens into the dry, warm room.

I breeze past Danny to Steve sitting at the coffee table. He raises his brow; Australian prison washboard lines cover most of his forehead. I turn back to Danny—his face is open for business.

I pat my distended belly. "The eagle has landed." I pull out the bag and toss it to Steve. Knowing but without knowing, all I wanted was Danny's and Steve's recognition and attaboys, the stuff Dad could never give. Deep down, I knew my only value to them was the money I fronted to make this rift possible. But I wanted so much more.

Ten years plus would pass before I would hit bottom. Like Danny and Steve, on my way down, I clung to whatever scraggly branches I could reach, in hopes of delaying my final descent to the rocks.

Either way, Jesus and his family ate well for a week after my visit.

Ilari Pass
in the basement
Poetry

a lock of hair and a picture is held tight,
crumbled like a treasured memory;
all that is left, braided, faded, separated
from her that he used to know and...
love...hate...in himself, that he used
to know and...love...hate...in her, that he used
to know and...love...hate...in the other, war,
in the village...women...children...back to her,
without her, there is no one like her
that he used to know and...love...hate...
forgetting, which he cannot...love...hate...
and pace, forward and back and around
in this empty space, feel the geometry
in the release on his inhale, the sharp crack,
the organized chaos of ricochet goes
straight to the heart, her face
drops to the floor, dust floating
in the entryway late afternoon sunshine
filtering through the window, looking out

for someone close; the dog runs and
pees on the pant leg of his uniform;
her nails scrabbled across the concrete
as she spun in circles and jumped
to lick his face

LA Brown
The Choir
Fiction

      Mr. Mann looked like an astronaut. A man of about 40, he was fit and lean with short black hair and straight small teeth. Every movement he made was deliberate and measured. I once watched a video of a robot from the Mitsubishi Corporation repeatedly opening and closing a car door and it made me think of him.

      To Mr. Mann singing was mathematics, each note calculated and arrived at precisely with zero tolerance for error. Our school choir comprised of fifteen pious children and me. A boy with blonde hair and blue eyes and pretty enough that I think that my contribution was intended to be aesthetic rather than aural because I couldn't sing. But I practiced hard.

      For the finale to our year-end assembly in July we were to sing *Que Sera, Sera* to the Grade 7 students who were leaving our elementary flock to go to middle school. In March, we began meeting in the school music room after our lessons on Mondays and Thursdays. Mr. Mann's method was repetition. It was *Que Sera, Sera* and *Que Sera, Sera* only that we sang, twice a week, for months. Stockholm syndrome set in and our little choir became like a cult. The cult of *Que Sera, Sera*.

      On the last Thursday practice before the Friday performance we were led to a makeshift stage in the library for our dress rehearsal. Mr. Mann chased out the librarians and closed the windows (lest we be heard prior to the event) and then set about chalk marking the positions on the stage where each of us were to stand at Friday's assembly. He then walked along our two lines of eight straightening our shoulders, lifting our chins and tapping our feet together with firm shoves from his polished black brogues. He then took his conducting position in front and lifted his hand readying us to start. He mouthed one, two, three and dropped his arm swiftly. We began singing.

When I was just a little girl
I asked my mother, "What will I be?
Will I be pretty, will I be rich?"
Here's what

Mr. Mann rose his hand sharply in a fist and we froze, immediately silent. A mistake so early into our rehearsal would be likely met with a clipped and sardonic reprimand. Instead, he looked directly at me and said "your voice has broken." And so, I was sent away. While I waited outside for my mother to collect me, I wondered about how broken voices are fixed and if I would need to go to the hospital. I also wished that my mother was Doris Day.

Anita S. Pulier
Memo
Poetry

> ...I love as I loved you
> young, except that, old, I am astonished
> at such a possibility, and am duly grateful.
> —Wendell Barry (VII, Leavings)

Hold me as we
navigate the inevitable.

Ignore unkind body parts
screaming warnings.

Laugh as though this is a joke and
we are the only ones in on it

.

Explore gratitude, regret,
anger, and joy—but quickly,

time rushes through illusive openings,

insists on recognition.

Stay alert,
keep the beast at bay

with sacrificial offerings of
champagne and flowery toasts.

Cue the music, snap lights off,
in the silky dark

re-explore me,
rediscover the miracle

of what once was
morphing into what is.

Tip your weathered hat, give a
nod to inexplicable luck.

Allow the wind at your back to
push you close, wrap your long

arms around me.
Whisper the L word

in a secret language
only we understand.

Kiss. Repeat.

Anita S. Pulier
Hiding in Plain Sight
Poetry

Stand by
admire those thick manes
rushing by.

Didn't we once avert
our gaze from greying heads,
insist on our own version of devotion?

Ahhh, what a gift of youth
is selective sight, offering
protection from the unmanageable,
a chance to delay the inevitable.

Toss those clichés about the journey.
Don't name it, live it.
Ignore that carping GPS,
take the longer more congested route,

the one with the gorgeous views,
the one that takes forever,
the one that will probably
make you late for dinner,

ravenous.

Photograph by Jeff Talarigo

Rebecca Lee
The Benefits
Fiction

Mrs. Carter wondered what to wear for the annual art auction. This year the proceeds would be donated to the Mothers Without Privilege Fund: a committee she had joined not six months after her retirement. Without work to keep her busy, Mrs. Carter, along with several other newly-retired women, drank coffee in the community recreational center while discussing other people's finances.

"What do we name the auction?" an ex-nurse pondered the appropriateness of poverty description. "Art for Underprivileged Mothers?"

The word "underprivileged" struck Mrs. Carter as distasteful, but why, she couldn't articulate. "Underappreciated" was almost cute. "Less fortunate" still had a soup kitchen feel to it. One member of the committee worried that if the title sounded too much like church charity, nobody would find it fun. Finally, after a lengthy, but necessary debate, the committee agreed upon "underprivileged." This was a word they frequently heard when addressing unfortunate women.

The benefit was to be hosted at a dining hall in a once-conservative area in downtown Chicago. Mrs. Carter heard it used to be the kind of space where very young women, women in their early twenties, held fancy wedding receptions.

Mrs. Carter, married by the time she was 21, mused over the comings and goings of weddings, marriage, and age itself. It seemed even the word "early" appeared out of date

Mrs. Carter enjoyed the small things about marriage. She enjoyed watching Fred slowly eat his toast in the kitchen while they reached for different sections of the paper. They did things like "card night" at their neighbor's house on Tuesdays. Fred worked long hours and Mrs. Carter didn't mind. They had an amicable silence, she thought. There wasn't much left to say.

The dining hall had been purchased by an outside family decades ago. While it no longer required a jacket and tie for the men, Mrs. Carter was fine with that. Time went on. New customs became old. When viewing the establishment as a possible venue for the auction, Mrs. Carter thought the orangey-red glow of bar lights seemed almost exotic. The paintings that were already hanging on the walls looked strikingly similar to the art that would be auctioned off in just a little over 2 weeks.

After discussing it at length with the committee, Mrs. Carter decided to reserve the space.

"I'm sorry, ma'am. All booking is done in person," a manager said over the phone. Mrs. Carter cringed at the word "ma'am." Even now, after a full career once had and now ended, she still thought the word aged her ugly.

Personalized invitations had already been sent. The venue was approved by each artist. A quick call to reserve the space didn't seem like a difficult task, but now, once again faced with the prospect of downtown traffic, Mrs. Carter sighed heavily into the phone. "I guess I can come back," she said.

Mrs. Carter, reluctantly pulled on her black, button-down pea coat to drive the ten minutes to downtown. She didn't like downtown. There was a pervasive sense of dirtiness, even if the streets were swept. She could smell cigarette smoke and the vendors standing on every corner seemed to be yelling at her. Although she was sure the new shops and bought-out restaurants were just fine, she did notice the lack of well-dressed patrons in the area. Pulling her coat a little closer, she briskly stepped from her car to the dining hall without looking anyone in the eye.

"I'd like to reserve this space for the Saturday evening after next," Mrs. Carter said to the host. She looked for a place to put her coat, but found none.

"Your ID, ma'am." The same man over the phone held out his hand. He was busy staring at a glowing apple on his laptop.

Mrs. Carter reached into her pocketbook and pulled out her ID. From outside the front window, a man in a gray sweater and jeans paced back and forth. Sometimes he stared through the window. Other times he focused straight ahead.

"When did you want to book?"

Mrs. Carter sighed. "The Saturday evening after next."

The gray sweatered man stopped pacing and glanced through the window again. He put his hands inside his pockets and then took them out. He seemed anxious.

"It's $200 up front," the man said.

"What?"

"I need a deposit to rent you the space," he explained.

Mrs. Carter had heard about people trying to rip off women of a certain age. Her own sister had fallen prey to an internet scam that said her computer would die if she did not purchase special software. Once the software was installed, her credit card information was stolen. It had taken her months to get back on track.

"I've never heard of this," she said, although she was pretty sure she had.

"Yes, ma'am. It's standard around here."

"Well, I don't know about this."

"That's fine," the man said, closing his laptop and appearing to walk away.

"Where are you going?" Mrs. Carter asked.

"I need to close up soon. You can take a minute to decide what you want to do, but I want to leave here before five."

Mrs. Carter stared at a large canvas painted with blocks of color that vaguely resembled the Chicago skyline. "Fine," she said. "Let's just be done with it."

On her way out of the dining hall, Mrs. Carter felt somebody's eyes following her. She put her hands in her pockets. The sound of footsteps followed, almost completely in time with her own. She picked up her pace. In a modern furniture store that sold 70s couches, she glanced at the reflection behind her. The man in the gray sweater was close.

"Excuse me." She heard a man's voice behind her. He probably smelled like greasy food and alcohol. Mrs. Carter kept walking.

"Excuse me, miss," he said again. Mrs. Carter picked up the pace.

"Miss!" He said, practically shouting. Mrs. Carter knew he could tell she heard him, but refused to look in his direction.

"Hey, look!" The man's voice echoed violently. "Just listen to me!"

Mrs. Carter stared at the street corners around her, but found only the vendors staring back. Instinctually, she crossed her arms firmly around her chest and turned to face the sweater.

"Yes?" She said.

The man leaned against the side of the modern furniture store. His breath was ragged and she suspected he smoked cigarettes. "I don't have any money." Mrs. Carter clarified.

The man in the sweater stared for a beat longer than she expected. "I don't need money." He said. "I need to talk to the guy in the dining hall about my art display last month."

Mrs. Carter thought about the blocks of color and how they matched so perfectly with one of the auction pieces for sale. "Do you know where he went?"

Mrs. Carter stared at the gray sweater. He didn't smell like smoke. "I'm sorry," she said, but for what she wasn't entirely sure. "I don't know anything about that."

Mrs. Carter decided to wear a simple necklace to the auction.

Unlike some committee members, she didn't want to stand out with expensive accoutrements. Instead, Mrs. Carter retrieved a simple gold chain given to her by her husband from their first anniversary. Planning the event had occurred with such purpose, but faced with the idea of several hours in a dining hall downtown suddenly seemed exhausting. Mrs. Carter stood in front of her bathroom mirror while she rummaged through a box of jewelry. For the first time since retirement, she wondered whether to stay or go.

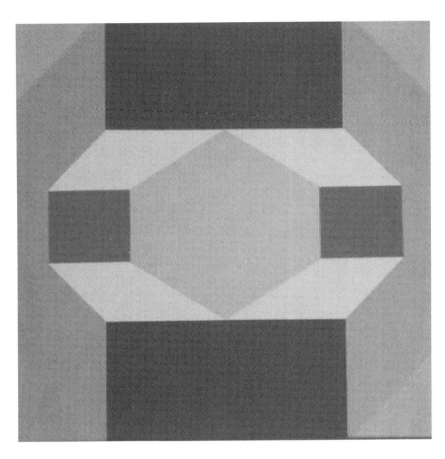

Painting by Carol MacAllister

John E. Simonds
The Ground Game
Poetry

We start to smell like a compost of life,
our quick sink soapings not doing the job.
Even with rails to hang onto,
our trips to the shower
seem hindered endeavors,
juggling bath wash in one hand
while keeping the other one free.
Lifting one foot,
then the other, to scrub,
feeling pain for disabled friends
and wondering how they get this done.
We start postponing daily essentials
and blaming the blades
for missing the hairs
tufting up in earlobes and nostrils
along cheeks, chins and lip lines.
We envision farmlands reverting to fields,
of grass not for smoking but just growing wild,
of weeds not for healing but sprouting

free in the untended furrows,
draining occasional orchards
lost in the last signs of care.
Growths spread their shoots with abandon,
returning the soil to a status of elders
lost in the memory of purpose.
We tread in end games, goals in the ground,
ploughing over forgettable moments
to rejoin our layered origins,
thinking more of the Earth
as the source of our time.

Neal Lipschutz
Thanks But No Thanks
Fiction

"This year, no Thanksgiving ," Leon told his son.

"What's that Dad? What about Thanksgiving?" Leon heard the exasperation in his son's voice. Loud and clear. Impatient. Was that new? Leon wondered. Was there something in Benjamin's growing up that should have tipped Leon to the adult appearance of this? What to call it? Attitude? Agitation? Leon didn't think there were any signs in the past, but the truth was he could no longer remember. Certain scenes from his children's youth were still clear. Leon diving into the upstate lake to grab struggling Sarah, who too much trusted her swimming strength. Benjamin fighting back tears as he slipped and stood, slipped and stood, moving so slowly and awkwardly on the ice during the hockey tryouts that meant so much to him that it gave Leon pains in his stomach that felt like stab wounds. There were other sharp scenes, but to Leon much of their childhood years were a blur.

Leon started again to speak, as slowly and clearly as he could. There was a shaky rasp that he couldn't lose no matter how many times he cleared his throat.

"I said you and your family don't need to stop by to see me on Thanksgiving morning. I free you of the obligation. It's not necessary."

"That's nonsense, Dad," Benjamin responded, a hint of anger now. "Of course it's necessary."

"Not necessary," Leon repeated.

"It is necessary. Families visit on Thanksgiving. That's what they do. Like it or not. Now, let's talk about something else. How do you feel?"

Leon felt lousy. Low energy. Some difficulty breathing. He couldn't use his legs at all. If he wanted to move, it was in a wheelchair. What he hated most was the dependency. Without the help of the staff at the assisted living facility in which he'd been ensconced for going on three years, Leon could not function.

"I'm fine," Leon said.

"Good, Dad, good to hear. Listen, I'm traveling for work next week and then David has a soccer tournament out of tow…"

"All good, take care of your family."

"So I won't be able to visit for a while. Not next weekend for sure. Maybe there's a weekday morning I could take off and come over. Don't know if Tuesday the 10th would work, maybe the 14th. I'll have to see."

"Don't worry about any of it," Leon said. Then he hung up the phone. He was tired. Benjamin was lost in his mental calendaring and didn't immediately notice.

Then, belatedly conscious of the silence, he said, "Dad? Dad!" When he got no response he shook his head and pressed his cell phone to end things from his side. The old guy was getting battier. Less and less with it. Trying to cancel Thanksgiving. Should he call him back? The call was pretty short, not the 15 minutes Benjamin tried to stretch toward as the minimum necessary as to count as legitimate contact from a dutiful son, one worthy of approbation. But there was no time for a call back. It was nearly 10 and Mindy's soccer game started at 10:30. Any moment now he expected his wife to yell to him to remind him of what he already knew: the rest of his Saturday morning was devoted to getting Mindy to her travel soccer game and then watching her team play.

"Benjamin!" The blast from wife Debbie reached him through

the closed doors of the den, which he used as a home office. Like clockwork, he thought. He didn't answer. Nobody said den anymore, did they? Benjamin idly wondered as he left room.

Leon slipped his cell phone into the pocket of his brown cardigan. Ah gosh, he means well. Shouldn't be so hard on Benjamin. Feels a lot of pressure, always did. Why? Who knows. Sarah was never like that. Benjamin and Sarah had an easy enough childhood. Good home, good schools. Both grown up before the divorce. No problems. Not objectively. But we create problems enough for ourselves, Leon knew. Don't need any help there. Why should his children be any different? They certainly weren't children anymore. Hadn't been for a long time.

The assisted living facility staff made seasonally appropriate attempts to keep the place cheerful. In October, that meant painting and pasting leaves of different fall colors on the hallway walls. The actual and the artistic brought together, rendering an autumn scene to spark the old people's memories.

"How do you like the fall decorations?" the facility's assistant director asked Leon as he sat with an open large-print novel near a window in the common room. His usual spot.

"Very nice," he answered, not looking up.

"Would you like some leaves to decorate the walls of your room?" she asked. "We gathered a lot of fallen leaves this year."

"Certainly not!" Leon growled.

The assistant director shrank back. Leon realized the unintended impact of his words. He shifted to a saccharine smile. "I wouldn't want to deprive the others of even a single leaf," he said, recovering his manners. "In my room, only I would be able to enjoy them." The assistant director accepted Leon's nonsensical explanation. She nodded, straightened up and moved away. "Chernox would see them too, of course," Leon said to her back. She didn't hear. Why can't they leave you in peace to read a book? Leon wondered. Why did they all think they weren't earning their salaries unless they constantly pestered you to cheer up, using voices usually employed on five-year-olds? No different than anyone else in that regard.

When Leon returned to his room, Chernox was there waiting for him. Leon had given him full access. Some patients made him wait outside their rooms if they weren't there. A severe insult as Leon saw it. It was time for Leon's daily cleaning. Midday wasn't an ideal time for a shower, but there were others to tend to and there was a schedule to follow. Leon refused to call or consider it a shower since he did not stand up. It was in fact a shower, even if Leon sat under the falling water in a specially designed chair. Chernox helped him undress and delicately maneuvered him into the chair. Afterwards, Chernox tactfully helped Leon reassemble.

"Chernox, you know I couldn't manage without you. I don't believe I always properly thank you."

"Yes, Mr. Leon," Chernox said, "You and all the other men on the floor. I take care of all of you."

"I hope you're well paid for it."

Chernox laughed. "You are a funny man, Mr. Leon."

"Even when I don't mean to be. Chernox, please call me Leon, not Mr. Leon. We are two men thrown together here. The fates would have it. You to work, me to die. First names are fully sufficient."

Chernox laughed again. "Yes, you are a funny man, Mr. Leon. I mean Leon."

"I like the way you say my name. It sounds like the city in France. Named for a lion, I guess. Elegant. A name for someone of great strength. Definitely not me. Not now."

Chernox loaded his cart and pushed it toward the door.

"One more moment, Chernox. You know, after much time, I don't even know where you are from."

"Trinidad and Tobago."

"Which one? Which island?"

"Trinidad."

"Ok. Good. Now I know. I am changing topics. If someone forced you right now to say something true about yourself, one completely true thing, what would it be?"

264

Chernox released his grip on the cart's handle. "A true thing," he said softly. He hesitated. And then, "I am a man of faith."

"And family?" Leon asked.

"Yes, that too. A wife and two girls, young. So, family too."

"Chernox, as a man of faith, if I could prove to you, absolutely prove that there is no God, what would happen to you? Would you still go home to your wife tonight? Would you show up at work tomorrow morning?" Leon did not have such proof in his back pocket, but he'd long taken as a given the absence of any God.

Chernox shook his head and smiled. "Faith, Leon, it is stronger than doubt."

"Ok, Chernox, ok, I get it. There's no talking sense to you on this topic."

"Like I said, you are a funny man Leon."

On Thanksgiving morning Benjamin showed up at the assisted living facility with his wife Debbie and son and daughter. It was 10 am. The plan, as it had been the prior two Thanksgivings during Leon's incarceration, was to spend an hour with him before heading off to a large and more traditional Thanksgiving at Debbie's sister's place. It was a couple hours' drive, so they didn't want to start out too late.

Once introductory pleasantries were exchanged, Benjamin's son David, 14, pulled out his cell phone. His daughter Mindy, 11, her iPad. Over-the-ear headphones were quickly attached by each child.

Benjamin asked Leon how he was feeling.

"Good, thanks. No complaints." After a silence, Leon asked, "How's business?"

"Good," Benjamin said. "No complaints there, either."

"You look well Leon," his daughter-in-law said. "Unlike the rest of us, you don't seem to age."

Leon snorted. "Yeah, I figured out how to live forever. Sitting around here doing nothing is actually the key to the fountain of youth. I must be on to something."

The assistant director of the assisted living facility knocked and then opened the door, sticking half her body into the room. She said to

Leon, "I know your son and his family can't stay to join us for the group Thanksgiving lunch. But if you like, I can probably coax the kitchen staff into preparing some turkey and fixings early so you can share some food together."

"God, no!" Leon shouted. "No turkey for breakfast."

The assistant director shrank back in reaction to his harshness. Leon felt the same sting from hurting her without intent. He changed his tone. "It's very kind of you to offer, but they will eat turkey later today and I look forward to joining the regular group for lunch." The assistant director nodded and backed out of the room.

"I like the Thanksgiving décor," Debbie said. "It brightens up the room." She nodded toward the mobiles comprised of paper turkeys and Pilgrim figures that hung from the ceiling above Leon's dresser.

"They're terrible. It looks like a baby's room with mobiles," Leon said. "If I could stand up, I'd tear them down. No one who works here will do it for me, not even Chernox. They're all afraid they'll get in trouble."

"Oh, come on, Leon," Debbie said. "It's nice."

Benjamin asked Leon if Sarah had called.

"Not today," said Leon. "They don't know Thanksgiving over in England."

"Yeah, but Sarah's not English," Benjamin said. "No matter how long she lives there or how much she wants to be." He resented his sister for living so far away and leaving all Leon-related matters to him. "When was the last time you heard from her?"

"I get emails sometimes," Leon said.

"Emails? You read emails?"

"Once Chernox set it all up for me I do. Quite easy, really."

"And you email back to Sarah?"

"Yes I do."

There was silence. Then Leon asked Benjamin to have the children remove their headphones. "I want to ask them a couple things." After some gesturing, Benjamin got the message across and the children complied.

"How's school?" Leon asked.

Fine, they said.

"How's soccer?"

Fine, they said.

"Do you have any questions for me?" Leon asked. "I've lived a long time and seen a lot of things." David shook his head no and put his headphones back on. Mindy asked, "What's it like not to be able to walk?"

"Mindy!" her mother shrieked.

"That's all right, Debbie. Let her be. It's a good question, best thing said all morning. Straight up: it's bad. Real bad. I know there are worse things that happen to people. Much worse. I've read about a lot of them. I've witnessed a few of them. So there's that. And some people do fine. Do great things even if they don't walk. But for me, at my age, it's plain bad."

"Oh, Leon," Debbie said. "Everything with you is G-L-O-O-M."

Leon wondered why Debbie spelled it but did not speak the word. Did she not want the children to hear it put together? Was gloom too ugly for young ears? Surely they knew the word and its meaning. And they could spell. Public education couldn't have deteriorated that much. David had his headphones on in any case. Mindy didn't strike Leon as the fragile type.

Benjamin looked at his watch. Time to go, he announced. David heard his father this time, even through the headphones. Benjamin's family stood as one.

"See you soon," Benjamin said to his father.

"No doubt," Leon replied.

Photograph by Jeff Talarigo

Holly Tappen
Mrs. Edgewater Goes to Jamaica
Fiction

Without wanting to, Mrs. Edgewater got in the boat. Her friends, Astrid and Raja, looked excited, happy to be there. Although the sky was gray and the sea was high, this day had been planned all year. The big black captain smiled at her, easy-going. No constraints. She smiled at everybody in their unfamiliar, colorful bathing suits. *Try to have a good time*. Uncharacteristically, all Mrs. Edgewater really wanted to do was flop into a comfy beach chair and veg. She did not feel vacationy at all.

The earthquakes that hit Puerto Rico were churning up the Caribbean, turning it colder and murkier. She had never been in a glass-bottomed boat: she gazed through a window to the other half of the world. Blue. Sandy bottom.

The captain started the motor and pulled away from the resort, away from the bar, restaurant, and pools. The tall waves made her glad that she never got seasick, but she had stowed some antacids in her beach bag just in case. The coastline was beautiful. As they headed up past the point, the beach gave way to rocky cliffs. Pirates used to shelter here and bury their treasures in caves.

The cave was deep, mysterious, and slightly too small for the 32-foot boat to safely enter, with those waves. The captain lowered the anchor nearby and handed out the snorkeling masks. There were no fins

269

or life jackets. Just as well. Mrs. Edgewater had been a competitive swimmer in grade school and high school, as comfortable in water as on land. There was now a magical place when she looked in the window: tropical fish, sand, and scalloped rocks created a blue and green ecosystem that she wanted to become part of, despite her mood. The bottom was far away.

Splash. Raja jumped in. *Crash*, as Astrid followed. Her turn.

Slowly, Mrs. Edgewater removed the warm towel from around her shoulders and stood up.

"Come on, Edge," Raja shouted. "It's beautiful..." as she turned to swim inside the cave.

Mrs. Edgewater took a shallow dive.

Cold. Cold and so wet. Horribly salty water seeped into her mouth as she gasped. No air entered her lungs. Treading water, she ripped off the mask and goggles, trying to breathe. *Air.* She needed air. She struggled towards the cave.

Her friends were far away. The boat seemed impossibly far. Inside the cave there was no beach, just ledge after ledge of rock. A wave washed over her head and stung her eyes. She swallowed water. Trying to swim, but achieving only a dogpaddle, Mrs. Edgewater reached for a rocky outcropping. She grabbed the top edge of the rock but it cut her hand. Over the centuries, the water had scalloped out carvings in the rock, leaving sharp edges. But she was desperate.

She put both hands out. A wave lifted her up, then forced her downward into the cutting edges. She was pressed against the enemy rock. Her lungs did not work. She turned toward the boat and saw an enormous wall of water heading for her. With all her remaining strength, she pushed out into the wave, but it dashed her backwards. She saw, rather than felt, the submerged rock cut a double line down the back of her thigh. A ribbon of blood wafted into the sea.

Can't sharks smell blood in the water?

Get to that boat.

It's so hard.

Get to that boat.

She gasped again like a fish thrown upon a pier. Her lungs were empty as the air she gulped failed to reach them. She envisioned herself floating peacefully down 20 feet below, moving gently like an anemone, with the graceful flow of Ophelia. *It would be so easy to slip under.* But then she would be dashed against the rocks. She thought of her son, 30 years old now. In her mind, he was 12 and he admired her.

No.

Get to that boat.

She remembered her swimming days. *What had they taught in lifesavers class? Oh yes. Float. Float.* Counterintuitively, she flipped over and arched her back. Another wave broke in her face. She heard the captain yell:

"Are you okay?"

No, she mimed. Would he jump in and save her? He looked very concerned. Oddly, she was embarrassed and hoped her friends would not think she was drowning. Her throat ached as though she had been crying for hours. Days. She began a weak flutter kick away toward the boat.

She saw the clouded sky through the level of water in her face. She was on her own. Her chest hurt unlike any other experience she had ever had.

The captain threw a lifejacket into the sea. It plopped nearby, yet so far away. She batted toward it like a sick kitten with a toy. With a slow whip kick, Mrs. Edgewater reached it and hauled it under her.

It was a little bit better. Air came into the lungs with sweet relief, but it left too quickly.

"Are you okay?" the captain called again.

"No," she peeped. He threw the ladder over the edge of the boat: she had a goal. Another quick breath. She was very weak. She grabbed the ladder. *Safe.*

Safe? She could not pull herself up to the steps. As she held up her arm, the captain caught her wrist. With one powerful motion, he pulled her up from the water and swung her gently to the deck. *Cold air.* Unable to stand, she tried to lay down. That was worse. She tried over and over for a full breath but could only pant. She sat upright with a yogic straight back and tried to relax her throat. It hurt as if she had

Photograph by Holly Tappen

swallowed a balloon full of salted ocean.

In swim team they used to feel for their pulses in between races. Mrs. Edgewater put her two middle fingers on her wrist and felt for her heartbeat. Nothing. She felt the vein in her throat. No response. Was she dead? A zombie? Where was her old reliable heart?

Blood streamed down her leg, diffused with water. She did not feel a thing but the pain in her chest. The captain pulled out the emergency first aid box. He grabbed the bottle of rubbing alcohol and patiently poured it over her wounds from the rocks. She vaguely watched him and wondered why it did not sting like crazy. She tried to regulate her breathing but it was impossible; the breaths came in gulping heaves.

Suddenly, she felt sick to her stomach. *Oh great.* She must have looked green because the captain asked her once more if she was okay. *Nope.*

"Are you going to throw up?" he asked nervously. She nodded and moved to the far side of the little boat. She did not want to barf into the pristine waters of the pirate cave. But nothing upchucked.

As she sat back, trying to breathe more easily, her eyes wandered out to her friends swimming in their own worlds. Oh, no. Raja was too close to those sharp walls. One wave would crush her into the rocks. Mrs. Edgewater squeaked and the captain followed her arm out to Raja. He whistled loudly and Astrid, who was closer, heard him. She looked at the boat and saw the captain signaling Raja.

"She is too close. She is too, too close," he shouted in his thick accent.

Astrid glided quickly to Raja and touched her shoulder. Raja popped up, surprised, pulled out of the wonderland that Mrs. Edgewater had missed. Together, the friends swam back to the boat and easily climbed aboard.

"Are you okay?" Astrid asked Mrs. Edgewater. Pale, shaky, she shrugged. The captain had felt her pain, she thought, and managed a smile.

They passed the high rocks where cliff divers jumped. There was a crowd up top, drinking their cocktails from plastic cups, and a smaller crowd in the water. A body slapped into the water as people clapped and cheered. Mrs. Edgewater gazed at the cliffs with longing. She should jump. She had loved the high diving board back at the old pool. It would be an adventure. But she saw the distance she would have to swim to get to the staircase that led to the jumping off place. *No.*

"I'm going to jump," Raja announced as she hiked up her straps and threw down her towel. "Edge, are you coming?"

No.

Raja dove into the aquamarine water and swam confidently towards the cliff. Mrs. Edgewater fondly watched her go.

Next year. Mrs. Edgewater promised herself. *Yes.* She was determined to survive. Exercise. Eat right. Take Tai Chi. Because next year, like Raja, she would jump from those rocks into the sea.

Jennifer Lagier
Summer Serenade
Poetry

> *"I can hear the almost unhearable sound of the roses singing."*
> *~ Mary Oliver, "How I Go to the Woods"*

Creamy floribundas croon from barrel halves,
seduce cruising bumble bees,
waft erotic perfume upon summer breeze.
Fading mauve and pink petals
tumble like spent confetti to organic mulch,
transform garden beds into fragrant mosaics.
Scarlet roses intertwine redwood trellis.
Hummingbirds plunder sweet, swollen blooms
as lazy swallowtails fondle yellow lantana.

Photograph by Jeff Talarigo

Alex Jordan
Stitches
Fiction and Photography

I'd promised myself I wouldn't get caught in this again. It wasn't worth it. This melancholy that arises inside you in an instant, as quickly as a chance encounter, and that takes you months to let go afterwards. I couldn't endure it another time; it was too much to take. I had to focus on more important matters. My grades weren't too good at school and my parents were worried. My teachers had told them I didn't show interest in any of their classes, and that my mind often appeared to be somewhere else. I couldn't argue with that. I said I'd make an effort, and I sincerely meant it. But what can I tell you? I saw her again that day, and I couldn't think of anything else.

I don't even know how we'd originally met. All I remember is when she'd looked me in the eyes for the first time. Oh my, it'd hit me so hard. The rest is a blur, really. It could've been the previous summer, the previous day or a million years before. I can't tell. We hadn't spoken, but something had happened and nothing would convince me otherwise. I may have been keen on making things up in my head, but not this. Something had happened, I knew it. Something stronger than the Earth we walked upon, residing in the fragile and furtive spark of a glimpse.

And the whole human history had seemed to be squeezed in there. Decades and centuries of evolution in a pulse, and believe me, there is no making it up. It overwhelms you so abruptly, all you can do is remain still and silent like an idiot. Like *her* idiot, and this deeper instinct that it's all you'll ever want to be.

Some call it teenage love, but looking back on it now, there'd been more to it. I don't really know what, but there definitely had. Not enough, though. We probably were too young. It hadn't been that long we'd started to discover the doubts hiding within ourselves. We wouldn't know yet how to deal with them, let alone with each other's. I later became aware that no one ever fully does, but still, it'd been way too

early, too big and too beautiful for us both. We'd let it drown under tears that wouldn't come out, and that'd been it. There'd been nothing else to say. We'd grown apart, met other people, and the bleeding wound had gradually turned into scar. One of many others to come, I'd try to tell myself. But I knew it wasn't that simple.

So, I met her again that day, and I couldn't think of anything else. The spark was still there, somewhere, but it wouldn't show. Maybe it couldn't. Was it only a hope? You spoke a few words, but you knew they were only meant to avoid a silence that neither of you could bear. And it was like all you'd shared, the parts of yourselves you'd given to each other, had been turned into the nullity of this empty talk. You'd become strangers. Two wandering souls whose embrace, lost among the abstractions of a daily life, had to be walked away from, and there was no going back. You were both aware of it, so you'd left it there and parted ways again. Alone with the undeniable truth of a loss, ungraspable and yet so real, it was like none of this had ever existed. She and I. These several months spent together, and this forgotten fire that left no heat behind. Not even ashes. I couldn't take it off my mind. How was it even possible?

Unable to get my head around it, I decided to take the dog out for a walk, thinking it might do me some good. But it started to get darker and darker around me, slowly framing me with a shadow that I knew all too well. It'd come back to swallow me again, just like it had after the breakup. Buildings seemed taller, streets more narrow. All the windows had been deserted.

I was on my own, trapped in a story that wasn't meant to be written. We'd had so little to live, and yet so much to give. This was all nothing now. Maybe it'd never been, and the thought of it actually brought me comfort. Wasn't it the only way for this memory to remain intact? That of her gentle eyes reflecting their brightness on mine for the first time, creating a temporality of their own and silently shouting all the beauty of the world. It was probably better like this, and I was feeling grateful all of a sudden.

Grateful, and alive. I wasn't gonna let that shadow get me. Oh no. I'd escape it. I'd run like I'd never have run before, as long as my breath would allow it, no matter the pain. I'd just run, not to a nothing that could have been everything, but to everything contained in this nothing that we shared for a while, and the stitches in my sides, both tearing and mending me up, would never have felt so good.

Christine Andersen
The Thing about Grief
Poetry

The thing about grief is
it's inconvenient

the way it lingers
like a party guest
who won't go home.

Mine is an old coat
with deep pockets
and holes that my memories
are slipping through,
tattered along the collar,
stained at the elbows
from leaning against the fence
bathed in
the setting sun,
a fire
behind the leafy limbs
of summer trees.

Grief is like that sunset, too,
a blaze spreading
until I flame red and orange,
sizzling, burning,
sinking down
into invisible.

Then it is the
darkness rising,
streetlights flickering on
like candles in a vigil.
I listen to my footsteps
on the sidewalk,
their steady drumbeat
in my lone procession
tramping forward
because there's nowhere else to go.

Christine Andersen
Shoveling Snow
Poetry

It's a moving meditation.

Bend, slide, scoop, toss.

Repetition.

Shoveling a path,
digging it wider

snowflakes gently
drifting

like thoughts,

piles mounting
around you

like wisdom.

Photograph by Brigitte Carroll

Our Contributors
Photography by Jeff Talarigo

Christine Andersen I am a retired dyslexia specialist who lives in a small town in CT near the woods. I have turned my attention to writing full time. I recently earned the distinction of being among the semi-finalists in the 2019 Concrete Wolf Poetry Contest for a book called *Neighborhood Poems*.

Watched by crows and friend to salamanders, **Lisa Bledsoe** is a hiker, beekeeper, and writer living in the mountains of Western North Carolina. A lifelong freelance writer, she started writing poetry in the spring of 2018. Her first book of poetry, *Appalachian Ground*, was published in 2019. A second book, *Wolf Laundry*, will be published in 2020, and she has new poems forthcoming

in *The Main Street Rag, Front Porch Review*, and *Jam & Sand*, among others.

LA Brown is an Australian poet and short prose writer living in the south-west of England near Bristol. He was raised in the port town of Fremantle, Western Australia, before moving to England in his early twenties. The ocean and the connection of memory to place, particularly port towns and cities, feature prominently in his writing. He performs poetry and vignettes of prose in Bristol and London.

A latte loving high school English teacher, **Lauren Burstein** draws inspiration from many writers including Joan Didion, Sandra Cisneros, and Lord Byron. She'll inch through rush hour traffic to see the ballet or an off-Broadway show, and her dog, Winston, may have been named after Orwell's hero. She found *Parasite* to be one of the most thought-provoking films she's ever seen, and she hopes to collaborate on a film project one day. Her ultimate hope is that she writes her own truths authentically. And while she is passionate about writing and teaching, her favorite job is being an aunt.

Matthew Byrne My poetry was featured in *The Best American Poetry 2007*. I have been nominated twice for a Pushcart Prize, and received an International Merit Award from *Atlanta Review* in 2009. My chapbook, *Silent Partner*, won the 2013 Sow's Ear Press Chapbook Award. I received an MFA in poetry from the University of Montana in 1999, and now serve as vice president at an insurance agency in Chicago.

Travis Cannell I am a graduate of University of California, Santa Barbara, where I studied computer science and worked as a reporter for the school newspaper. Currently, I work as a marketing consultant. I have been dedicated to studying my craft through weekly workshops and regional conferences/events and won the "Debt of Honor International Writer's Workshop: 2018 Award." When I'm not writing, I'm busy sailing, boating, or flying an airplane. My work has been published in *Playboy*

Online and *Red Savina Review.*

Brigitte Carroll, a native New Yorker, is currently being held captive in deepest, darkest suburbia. There, she hones her skills to make anything out of paper, yarn, or cookie dough. Really. Anything. Except the rest of her book, which is being difficult.

Wendy Carrus: I am a native New Yorker born in and partially raised in the Brooklyn Projects of the 60s. My eclectic exposure to different worlds moved me to pursue a career working with emotionally challenged youth. I began my career in Special Education and completed it with a Masters in Clinical Social Work from Columbia University. In motherhood I found a comforting and challenging life. Now I spend my time exploring my surroundings as they reveal their beauty.

William Cass has had over 200 short stories accepted for publication in a variety of literary magazines such as *J Journal, december, Briar Cliff Review,* and *Zone 3.* He was a finalist in short fiction and novella competitions at *Glimmer Train* and *Black Hill Press,* has received three Pushcart nominations, and won writing contests at Terrain.org and *The Examined Life Journal.* He lives in San Diego, California.

Jean Colonomos is an award-winning playwright and poet. Her plays have been produced in New York City, Los Angeles, Edinburgh, and regionally. Her poetry has been published online at yourdailypoem.com and in several journals—*Askew, Third Wednesday, Inkling, Spillway* and the *American Writers Review* where three of her poems about her dance career won honorable mentions. She also writes with Ann Buxie and they've been featured readers at the EP Foster Library, the Ojai Library, the Library of Thousand Oaks and Beyond Baroque. Her chapbook is *Art Farm* published by Finishing Line Press. Other credits include serving on Los Angeles' Cultural Arts panel and as PEN USA judge. For more go to jeancolonomos.weebly.com.

Charlotte Crowder lives and writes on the coast of Maine. She is a medical writer and editor by day. She is a previous contributor to *American Writers Review*. Among others, her short stories have appeared in *Intima, Maine Boats, Homes and Harbors, The Maine Review*, and *Brilliant Flash Fiction*. Forthcoming are short stories in *Dirigo Dreams Anthology* (City View Press) and *Anthology 2, Dreamers Creative Writing*. Her first picture book, *A Fine Orange Bucket*, was released by North Country Press in June 2019.

Alexandra Dane writes memoir, essay and blog (alexandradanewrites.com) based on her life's work with death and dying. Her essay, "Found. Well." is about traveling to heal. Her work has been published in The WritersWorkshopReview.net (*The Bitter and The Sweet*) and Lunch Ticket (*Somebody. Still*). Alexandra Dane's manuscript-in-progress is about coming of age—twice—at the mercy of cancer; once as a young caregiver and then as a patient. She is grateful for the two lives. She is well

Wendy Lynn Decker: I am the author of *Sweet Tea*, a novel and freelance writer with publications in *Cup of Comfort, American Writers*

Review, and *Mental Gladiator*. I also possess a Master's Degree in Creative Writing and spent two intermittent years teaching English Composition on Navy ships while traveling through Asia and Europe. I'm working on several writing

projects as well as teaching at a community college in New Jersey. You can learn more about me at: http://www.wendylynndeckerauthor.com

Richard Dokey's stories have won citations, prizes and awards in places like *Best American Short Stories, Best of the West* and the Pushcart Prize. He has novels and story collections to his credit. *Pale Morning Dun*, an earlier collection, published by University of Missouri Press, was nominated for the American Book Award and the PEN/Faulkner Award, *Fly Fishing The River Styx*, his new collection, was released by Adelaide Books in December 2018 to good reviews

Jon Epstein My work can be found in *Abstract: Contemporary Expressions, Crack the Spine, The Coachella Review, Poeticdiversity, Foliate Oak, Forge Journal, Sanskrit, Penmen Review, Poydras Review, Pilcrow & Dagger, Poetry Super Highway,* and *Santa Fe Writer's Project Quarterly.* I am a member of The Los Angeles Poets & Writers Collective. I am an emerging writer and a fine artist inspired by the daily trials and joys of simple life—as well as a father, musician, surfer, and recovering alcoholic. I live in the San Fernando Valley with my wife of thirty-two years.

D Ferrara, editor, has been a writer, editor and collaborator for more years than she cares to remember. She is honored to be the editor of *American Writers Review* and *Art in the Time of Covid-19,* among other publications.

Amelia Hope Florio is a student at Howell Middle School North. She is part of a competitive dance team at Freehold Academy of Performing Arts. She has competed as a Jersey Shore Idol at the Jersey Shore Arts Center. She enjoys swimming, bike riding and talking for hours on her iPhone.

Patricia A. Florio, founder, can map out Brooklyn by pizza parlors. Obsessed with publishing a literary journal like the *Paris Review,*

289

Patricia heeded her teacher's advice: "aim higher than the bull's-eye, in case you fall short." After putting herself through court reporting college and a career as a court reporter, she gathered enough stories to write books for the rest of her life. She earned two Norman Mailer scholarships (2012) and (2014), a BA from Rutgers University and an MFA from Wilkes University. Her memoir, *My Two Mothers*, (Phyllis Scott Thomas, 2010) is about her mother and aunt who raised her. Her website is patriciaflorio.com. She lives with her husband Ralph of 47 years in New Jersey where she co-founded The Jersey Shore Writers.

Ana M. Fores Tamayo An underpaid academic, I wanted to do something that mattered: I advocate for refugee families from Mexico and Central America. Working with asylum seekers is heart wrenching, satisfying, and humbling. My labor has eased my own sense of displacement. I have published in *Acentos Review*, *The Raving Press*, *Rigorous*, *Indolent Books*, *Chaleur Magazine*, *Memoir*, *Poxo Press*, *K'in*, *The Laurel Review*, *Down in the Dirt* magazine, *Twist in Time*, *Selcouth Station Press* in England, *Frontera* from Spain, *Literary Yard* in India, *Cosmographia Books*, the *Watchung Review*, *Lamplit Underground*, the *Toho Journal*, *Crossways* in Ireland, and *Jam & Sand* in Canada. I have photography published in *Acentos Review* and the *Bozalta Collective*, digital photography with poetry at UC Davis, and art exhibits which sold my work to benefit the Northern Manhattan Coalition for Immigrant Rights as well as Opening Doors International Services at the Oak Cliff Cultural Center.

Brandon French has been (variously) assistant editor of *Modern Teen Magazine*, a topless Pink Pussycat cocktail waitress, an assistant professor of English at Yale, a published film scholar, playwright, and screenwriter, Director of Development at Columbia Pictures Television, an award-winning advertising copywriter and Creative Director, a psychoanalyst in private practice, and a mother. Seventy-seven of her stories have been accepted for publication. She's been nominated twice for a Pushcart. She was an award winner in the 2015 Chicago Tribune

Nelson Algren Short Story Contest, and her short story collection, *If One of Us Should Die, I'll Move to Paris* is now available on Amazon.

Molly Fuller is the author of the full-length collection *For Girls Forged by Lightning: Prose & Other Poems* (All Nations Press) and two chapbooks, *Tender the Body* (Spare Change Press) and *The Neighborhood Psycho Dreams of Love* (Cutty Wren Press). Her work has appeared in *Nothing to Declare: A Guide to the Flash Sequence*, *100 Word Story*, *Blue Earth Review*, *Kestrel*, *NANO Fiction* and *Pedestal Magazine*. Fuller was a

Finalist for the Key West Literary Seminar Emerging Writer Award. She received her MFA from Sarah Lawrence College and is currently a doctoral candidate (ABD) in Literature at Kent State University.

Cindy Waszak Geary is a public health/social scientist turned creative nonfiction writer who focuses on memoir, social justice, and the natural world. Her first book, *Going to School in Black and White: A dual memoir of desegregation*, co-authored with LaHoma Smith Romocki, was published by Light Messages. She finds creative expression through photography and is working on a project combining words and images to explore how the lives of her ancestors have informed her own. Cindy is the mother of two grown children, Emily and Max, and has a three-year-old granddaughter, Daisy. She lives in Chapel Hill with her husband, Ron.

Charnjit Gill I have an MA in Creative Writing and a BA in English Literature & Creative Writing. I am a private tutor and have been a spoken word artist for 4 years. I was a member of The Writing Room. My work has been published in the *London Spoken Word Anthology 2015-2016* by Gug Press, *Typishly, Minerva Rising Press, From Whispers to Roars, KYSO Flash,* and *Ghost City Press.*

Susan Eve Haar Recently I received a Sloan Foundation commission for a new play. I have had a play up in Los Angeles, Saugertis, and my short play *No Time for Baby* was just published in *The Best 10-Minute Plays of 2018.* My monologues have been included in *Radical Thinking: Inside a Box*, published by Smith and Kraus; *Best Women's Monologue 2018*; and *Best Men's Monologues 2018*, among others. My fiction has appeared in *bluestem, Citron Review, Columbia Journal, Forge, Glint Literary Magazine, North Dakota Quarterly, Saint Ann's Review, Stonecoast Review,* and *Yemassee Journal.* I am a member of The Actors Studio, Ensemble Studio Theatre, and HB Playwright's Unit, as well as the Writer's Guild East.

Lenore Hart, a novelist and poet who also writes as Elisabeth Graves, is the author of *Waterwoman, Ordinary Springs*; *Becky: The Life and Loves of Becky Thatcher, The Raven's Bride, Black River,* and *Devil's Key*, and series editor of *The Night Bazaar* dark fantasy anthologies. Her books for young readers are *T. Rex at Swan Lake* and *The Treasure of Savage Island.* Hart has lectured or been writer-in-residence at Elizabethtown College, Flagler College, Florida State University, The Irish Writers Centre, The Norman Mailer Center, George Mason University, New College, Old Dominion University, The U.S. Naval Academy, and the Oberpfalzer Kunstlerhaus in Bavaria, Germany. She's been recognized by the NEA, The Virginia Commission for the Arts, The Virginia Center for the Creative Arts, The Florida Fine Arts Council, Old Dominion University and the Connecticut Poetry Society. Her work has been featured on Voice of America Radio, in *Poets and Writers*, and on the PBS series "Writer to Writer." She teaches in the Maslow Graduate Creative Writing Program, and at the Ossabaw Island Writers Retreat.

Barbara Schilling Hurwitz is a veteran teacher who has found a new voice through creative writing. Her stories have been published in *Montgomery Magazine, The Drabble, Fewer Than 500* and *Microfiction Monda*y. She lives in Bethesda, Maryland, with her husband.

Sabrina Ito: I am an emerging poet. I live in Honolulu, Hawaii, where I work as a Middle School Languages teacher. I have been writing and publishing poetry for close to a decade now. My poems have appeared in literary journals, such as *Bamboo Ridge, Clarion Magazine, West Trade Review, Coachella Review*, and *Blazevox,* among others. I am also the author of two poetry chapbooks, *The Witches of Lila Springs* (Plan B Press) and *Messages from Salt Water* (Finishing Line Press).

Thomas Penn Johnson was born in Greensboro, North Carolina. He received a B.A. in Classical Studies from then-Concordia Senior College, an M.A. in English from UNC-G, and continued graduate studies in English literature and history. A caseworker for the Cook County Department of Public Aid—Children's Division, he published a collection of poems entitled *If Rainbows Promise Not in Vain*. In 2009 he retired from Edison State College in Fort Myers, Florida after serving for 26 years as an instructor of English and humanities. He continues to write poetry and fiction.

Alex Jordan: After completing my MA in film studies in London, I left the academic world and worked on video editing projects, quickly specialising in mashups of archive footage. The whole process of it fascinated me: digging for small bits here and there that may have seemed trivial, and giving them some new life through edits, rhythmical plays, and interaction with other images, sounds and music. Unexpectedly, this search for potential sparks among the mundane finally led me to another practice: street photography.

Richard Key is a pathologist who lives in south Alabama with his wife and over-indulged cat. He began writing short stories and essays about twelve years ago, and his work has appeared in several literary journals, including *Adelaide Literary Magazine, Bacopa Literary Review,*

The Broken Plate, Carbon Culture Review, Crack The Spine, Evening Street Review, Forge, Hawaii Pacific Review, and *HCE Review*. He hopes that his random and disparate stories will one day magically align into a cohesive collection. His website is: richardkeyauthor.com.

Sarah Key My creative writing life began in entertainment public relations where I wrote press releases that were pure fiction. My publication history includes cookbooks, essays on the *Huffington Post*, and poems in print and online, with poems in four anthologies, such as the recent *Nasty Women Poets*. My poems have also appeared in *The Georgia Review, Calyx, Poet Lore, Minerva Rising*, Poetry Center San Jose, *Tulane Review*, and *Tuesday; An Art Project*. After studying poetry at Frost Place, Cave Canem, and the Unterberg Poetry Center, I now learn from my students at a community college in the South Bronx.

Jennifer Lagier has published seventeen books, taught with California Poets in the Schools, edited the *Homestead Review*, edits

Monterey Poetry Review and helps coordinate the second Sunday reading series for the Monterey Bay Poetry Consortium. Her work appears in *From Everywhere a Little: A Migration Anthology, Fire and Rain: Ecopoetry of California, Missing Persons: Reflections on Dementia, Silent Screams: Poetic Journeys Through Addiction & Recovery*. Newest books: *Trumped Up Election* (Xi Draconis Books) and *Dystopia Playlist* (CyberWit). For a full list of her publications, please visit her website, jlagier.net or Facebook page: www.facebook.com/JenniferLagier/

Sheree La Puma is an award-winning writer whose personal essays, fiction, and poetry have appeared in or are forthcoming in *WSQ*, *Juxtaprose*, *Heron River Review*, *The Rumpus*, *Plainsongs*, *The Main Street Rag*, *I-70 Review*, *The London Reader*, Bordighera Press's *VIA: Voices in Italian Americana*, and *Pacific Review*, among others. She received an MFA in Writing from California Institute of the Arts and taught poetry to former gang members.

Rebecca Lee has published in a variety of magazines. Some publications include *Able Muse*, Harvard's *thirdspace* journal, *Existere Journal,* etc. Her essay, "Rules of Engagement," was listed in the *2017 Best American Essays* anthology.

Neal Lipschutz: My short fiction for young people and adults has appeared in several digital and print publications, including *American Writers Review 2019*.

Carol MacAllister has been publishing her short fiction, nonfiction, and poetry for over twenty-five years. She has edited several books and won awards and competitions. MacAllister holds three MAs in creative writing and two MFAs—Fine Arts and Fiction. Carol is completing a book-length memoir, *The Inconvenient Child*. She is completing her first novel, a historical tale of homeless Irish lads on the streets of New York City during the 1850s.

Judy L. Mandel is a writing coach, freelance editor, and Senior Editor at Kaylie Jones Books. She is the author of the New York Times Best Seller, *Replacement Child*. Judy's essays, articles, and short stories have appeared in *Kveller.com, 34th Parallel, The Tishman Review, Connecticut LIFE, ASJA Monthly, Complete Wellbeing Magazine, Connecticut Authors and Publishers Magazine, The Southampton Review,* and other publications.

Raul J. Mendez was born in Caracas, Venezuela, in 1973 and moved to the U.S. at a young age. After growing up in Miami, Mendez moved to Portland, Oregon, and attended PNCA (Pacific Northwest College of Art) where he received a BFA in Painting & Drawing in 1997. He has a vibrant art practice, and supports the habit by flying 747 for an international cargo airline. He spends time in cities and airports drawing his surroundings and their people.

Ria Moolgie: I'm a photographer, blogger who believes that life is all about perception. Perception is everything.

Olive Mullet: I am a retired Ferris State University English professor who taught composition and humanities for twenty-five years. My publications include "Les Voleurs" in *Red Cedar Review*; "No One Showed" in *Sliverofstone*; "Outside" in *Dark Matter*; "The Watched Pot" in *The Cossack Review*; "Mr. Cavendish" in *Cigale Literary Magazine*;

"Butterfly" in *Tour*; "The Mantra," "Voices," and "The Recording," in *Emerge Literary Journal*; "In Search of Death" in *Cleaver Magazine*, "No Jewels in the Jungle" in *outsideinmagazine.com*; "Ambush" in *brainofforgetting.com*; and "Harold and Muriel" in *Fredericksburg Literary & Art Review*. I am a book reviewer for newpages.com and write a quarterly column on current fiction trends.

Don Noel Retired after four decades' prizewinning print and broadcast journalism in Hartford, CT, I received my MFA in Creative Writing from Fairfield University in 2013. I have since published more than five dozen short stories and nonfiction pieces (including "Milestones" in *American Writers Review 2019*) but have two novellas and a novel still looking for publishers.

Jill Ocone is a regular contributor to *Jersey Shore Magazine* and several Jersey Shore Publications guidebooks. She has been writing since she was a teenager and her work has been published in the *American Writers Review 2019, The Sun, Everywhere, School Leader*, and *American Cheerleader Magazine*, to name a few. She recently completed her first novel titled *Chapter One-A Novel*. Jill shares her Jersey Shore home with her husband. In addition to a writer, she is also a high school journalism educator. When Jill isn't writing, reading, or teaching, you'll might find her riding her bicycle around town, searching for sea glass, or laughing with her nieces and nephews. You can find Jill online at jillocone.com, on Facebook and Instagram at @jillocone, and on Twitter at @jill_ocone.

Jen OConnor is proud to have had three pieces in *American Writers Review 2019* and other work in *Two Hawks Quarterly, Saved Objects, Imagine, Iris Brown Lit Mag, Medusa's Laugh Press, Persimmon Tree, Impossible Archetype, London Journal of Fiction, Sinister Wisdom,* and performed in spoken word events in Los Angeles. My play *The Girl Who Would Be King* was winner of Chicago's Pride Films & Plays Women's Words contest and is published and licensed by Stage Rights. *Dressing Robbie Temple* was semi-finalist in Ashland New Plays Festival. *Gayby's Playdate* won the LGBT Festival in LA and was produced in South Korea. Jen holds an MA from St. Louis University and an MFA in Theatre from Southern Illinois University.

Kirby Olson: I am up in New York State between Binghamton and Middletown in a town called Delhi. I go down to Paramus now and then to shop at the B&N and at IKEA and Trader Joe's. I have five or six books.

Three of them are about literary figures: one on Gregory Corso, one on Andrei Codrescu, and one on contemporary comic writers. I also have a novel about an academic who starts a circus in Finland, and a book of poems called *Christmas at Rockefeller Center* (WordTech 2015).

Originally from Maplewood, NJ, **Ilari Pass** is a retired maintenance worker of the United States Postal Service. She holds a BA in English from Guilford College of Greensboro, NC, and an MA in English from Gardner-Webb University of Boiling Springs, NC. She was awarded the *Broad River Review* Editors' Prize in Poetry Award for 2016 and 2017, and a Ron Rash Award in Poetry finalist for 2019. Other works appear or are forthcoming in *Drunk Monkey: Literature and Film, JuxtaProse Literary Magazine, Free State Review, Blue Mountain Review, The Raw Art Review, Cathexis Northwest Press, Common Ground Review*, and others.

Colin Pink's plays have been produced in London, New York City and Berlin. His poems and stories have appeared in a wide range of literary magazines such as: *Acumen, American Writers Review, Poetry Ireland Review, Aesthetica* and online at *Ink Sweat and Tears* and *The High Window*. His first collection of poems, *Acrobats of Sound*, is available from Poetry Salzburg. His second collection *The Ventriloquist Dummy's Lament* has been published by Against the Grain Press.

Anita S. Pulier is a graduate of New York University and New York Law School. After practicing law in New York and New Jersey, Anita served as a U. S. representative for the Women's International League for Peace and Freedom at the United Nations. Anita's poems have appeared online, in anthologies and in print journals. Her book *The Butcher's Diamond* and her chapbooks *Perfect Diet, The Lovely Mundane*, and *Sounds of Morning* are published by Finishing Line Press.

Nicolas D. Sampson I am a writer-producer based in the UK and Cyprus. My stories were published in *Panorama: The Journal of*

Intelligent Travel, *The Scofield*, and most recently *The Writers' Magazine* (Oct 2019). My short story "Appearances" will be published in the *Tales of Reverie Journal* next year and my short story "Flames and Shadows" (for *Panorama*) was nominated for a 2018 Pushcart Prize. My film projects include *Behind the Mirror* (writer/producer), *Vita and Virginia* (executive producer), and *Show Me the Picture: The Story of Jim Marshall* (executive producer).

Marian Kaplun Shapiro is the author of a professional book, *Second Childhood* (Norton, 1988), a poetry book, *Players In The Dream,*

 *Dreamers In The Play* (Plain View Press, 2007) and two chapbooks: *Your Third Wish* (Finishing Line, 2007) and *The End Of The World, Announced On Wednesday* (Pudding House, 2007). A Quaker and a psychologist, her poetry often embeds the topics of peace and violence by addressing one within the context of the other. A resident of Lexington, she is a five-time Senior Poet Laureate of Massachusetts. She was nominated for the Pushcart Prize in 2012.

John E. Simonds, a retired Honolulu daily newspaper editor, has lived with his family in Hawai'i for more than 40 years and previously was a reporter for newspapers from Washington, DC, and other cities. A Bowdoin College graduate and former East Coast and Midwest resident, he has been writing poems since the 1970s and is the author of two self-published collections, *Waves from a Time-Zoned Brain* (AuthorHouse) and *Footnotes to the Sun* (iUniverse). Thank you for being part of CLMP's world and also for providing this opportunity.

Alan Sincic A teacher at Valencia College, my fiction has appeared in *New Ohio Review, The Greensboro Review, Big Fiction Magazine, Hunger Mountain Journal, A-3 Press, The Gateway Review, Cobalt,* and elsewhere. I've earned my MFA at Western New England University and Columbia, served on the editorial board of the Columbia Review, and—back in the day—published a children's chapter book, *Edward Is Only A Fish* (Henry Holt) that was reviewed in the *New York Times,* translated into German, and recently issued in a Kindle edition.

Cynthia Singerman, a Florida native, is a writer living in San Francisco. She holds a bachelor's degree in English literature and Spanish, as well as a law degree from the University of Florida. Her work has appeared or is forthcoming *in HerStry, Streetlight Magazine, Menda City Review,* and *Litbreak Magazine.* Her first novel is out for consideration, and she is currently working on her second novel, set in Central Florida.

Ann Christine Tabaka was nominated for the 2017 Pushcart Prize in Poetry, has been internationally published, and won poetry awards from numerous publications. She is the author of nine poetry books. She has recently been published in several micro-fiction anthologies and short story publications. Her most recent credits are: *Burningword Literary Journal, Muddy River Poetry Review, The Write Connection, Ethos Literary Journal, North of Oxford, Pomona Valley Review, Page & Spine, West Texas Literary Review, The Hungry Chimera, Sheila-Na-Gig, Foliate Oak Review, Better Than Starbucks!, The Write Launch, The Stray Branch, The McKinley Review,* and *Fourth & Sycamore.*

Jeff Talarigo is the author of novels *In the Cemetery of the Orange Trees, The Pearl Diver, The Ginseng Hunter* and numerous short stories. A Pennsylvanian, he has received the American Academy of Arts and Letters Rosenthal Award and a 2005 Kiriyama Prize Notable Book of the American Library Association and was included in NPR's 2008 *Under the Radar*. He has been featured on NPR's Weekend Edition and awarded a Fellowship at the New York Public Library's Cullman Center for Scholars and Writers. His work has been published in five languages. His photography graced *American Writers Review* in 2018 and 2019.

Holly Tappen is often found in her art studios, swearing at the computer while eating Smarties. Influenced by Leonardo da Vinci and Picasso, she will be the world's first Abstract Realist when she figures out what that looks like. Holly has written seven plays and a memoir. Her writing appeared in the book *Jewels of San Fedele*. A million light years ago, she majored in philosophy at Emory University because there was no creative writing program. Although she wants art in every aspect of her life, the IRS does not appreciate this, so she specializes in bad jobs. And she has a cat.

Alla Umanskiy: I'm a writer, living and working in Atlanta. I'm also a mother to two strong-willed daughters and a wife to a hilarious husband.

John Urban graduated from San Jose State College, California, with a degree in Physics and minors in Philosophy and Creative Writing. He presently lives in San Jose, California. His poems have been published in *Broad River Review, Common Ground Review, Nebo: A Literary Journal, New Vision* (UK), *Reed Magazine, The Mobius Strip, Jet Fuel Review, Rolling Stone, SLAB,* and *Steam Ticket*. His interests and influences include Classical Metaphysics and Modern Spirituality—he considers his work to be in the Romantic tradition of Emily Dickinson, Hart Crane, and Wallace Stevens, but distinguishes it as Transcendental Romanticism

Sophie Stach Virgilio: After I retired in 2000, I joined a writers group in Asbury Park. I wrote about my experiences as a child during

Hitler's occupation of Poland during WWII. I eventually published my stories in 2019 in a book called *Goat in the Attic*.

Tommy Vollman is a writer, musician, and painter. For many years, he was a baseball player. He has written a number of things, published a bit, recorded a few records, and toured a lot. Tommy's work has been nominated for the Pushcart Prize and the *Best of the Net* anthology. His stories and nonfiction have appeared in *The Southwest Review*, *Two Cities Review*, *The Southeast Review*, *Palaver*, and *Per Contra*. He has some black-ink tattoos on both of his arms. He's working on a short story collection and has a new record, *Youth or Something Beautiful*. He currently teaches English at Milwaukee Area Technical College and prefers to write with pens poached from hotel room cleaning carts.

Eleanor Windman: During the past three years, I have participated in the San Miguel Literary Sala, Iowa Summer Writing Festival, and Women of Woodstock. I'm a retired designer who at eighty-two years old started writing to keep old age from blindsiding me—it worked.

Marshall Woodward is an internationally-translated poet, writing lyric and narrative poems that address the supernatural, old flings, and a few spaces he has inhabited. He aims to provoke conversation around various climate issues of the day; environmental, political, and beyond. He attended the Gulkistan Residency in summer 2019, where his collection 'Geodes' was collected and edited.

Brahna Yassky "How Swimming Saved My Life" is a stand-alone essay based on parts of my memoir *After the Fire*. I healed my 55% burned body and changed my life through art, love, and swimming. I won honorable mention for the 2018 Doheny Prize from the Center for Fiction, was a finalist for the 2019 Brooklyn Nonfiction Prize, had essays published in AARP's *The Girlfriend*, *Blood and Thunder*, *The Tribeca Tribune*. I have exhibited my paintings and art extensively including:

302

MOMA, The San Francisco Museum of Modern Art, The Hudson River Museum, Bali Purnati Center, commissions from the New York City Department of Health for mural and subway posters.

Orit Yeret is a writer, artist, and teacher. Born and raised in Israel, she currently lives in the U.S. Her work recently appeared in *The Borfski Press*, *Ink Pantry*, *Drunk Monkeys*, *Crack the Spine*, *Blue Lake Review*, *Steam Ticket*, *Avalon Literary*, *Evening Street Review*, *(mac)ro(mic)* and *The Magnolia Review*. Read and view more of her work at www.orityeret.com.

Dawn. North Dome, Yosemite National Park Photograph by Jeff Talarigo

"...in a person who entertains us, there is much we forgive."

- Curtis Sittenfeld

About Us

American Writers Review is a multi-genre literary journal published by San Fedele Press. We welcome writers, artists and photographers of all backgrounds, styles and experience levels, who want to explore their art with us.

www.AmericanWritersReview.com

Made in the USA
Middletown, DE
30 June 2020